OCR
RECOGNISING ACHIEVEMENT

HODDER
EDUCATION

Official Publisher Partnership

OCR DESIGN & TECHNOLOGY FOR GCSE

RESISTANT MATERIALS

DAVID CARLSON
HARRY KING
STEVE PINNOCK
EDITOR: BOB WHITE

HODDER
EDUCATION
AN HACHETTE UK COMPANY

Orders: please contact Bookpoint Ltd, 130 Milton Park, Abingdon, Oxon
OX14 4SB. Telephone: +44 (0)1235 8 27720. Fax: +44 (0)1235 400454.
Lines are open from 9.00am to 5.00pm, Monday to Saturday, with a 24-
hour message-answering service. You can also order through our website
www.hoddereducation.co.uk

If you have any comments to make about this, or any of our other titles,
please send them to educationenquiries@hodder.co.uk

British Library Cataloguing in Publication Data
A catalogue record for this title is available from the British Library

ISBN: 978 0 340 98196 2

First edition published 2009
Impression number 10 9 8 7 6 5 4 3 2
Year   2012 2011 2010 2009

Hachette UK's policy is to use papers that are natural, renewable and
recyclable products and made from wood grown in sustainable forests.
The logging and manufacturing processes are expected to conform to the
environmental regulations of the country of origin.

Cover photo from © Goodshoot/Corbis
Typeset by Fakenham Photosetting Ltd, Fakenham, Norfolk
Printed in Italy for Hodder Education, an Hachette UK Company, 338 Euston
Road, London NW1 3BH

CONTENTS

ACKNOWLEDGMENTS

Every effort has been made to trace and acknowledge ownership of copyright. The publishers will be glad to make suitable arrangements with any copyright holders whom it has not been possible to contact.

The authors would like to thank the following: Dixie Grammar School, The Boswells School and Haberdasher Aske School for providing examples of students' work.

The authors and publishers would like to thank the following for use of photographs and illustrations in this volume:

Figure 1.9 © Design Pics Inc./Alamy, Figure 1.10 © Digital Vision, Figure 1.12, Figure 1.11 George Doyle/Stockdisc/Getty Images, Figure 1.12 © Purestock, Figure 1.37 TechSoft UK Ltd, Figure 2.2 © The Carlin Company/iStockphoto.com, Figure 2.14 © Maurice van der Velden/iStockphoto.com, Figure 2.16a © anzeletti/iStockphoto.com, Figure 2.16b © Chris Elwell/iStockphoto.com, Figure 2.25a © Ahmad Faizal/iStockphoto.com, Figure 2.25b RTimages/iStockphoto.com, 2.26 Photodisc/Getty Images, 2.27 © Tom Fewster/iStockphoto.com, Figure 2.28 © vnlit – Fotolia.com, Figure 2.29 © xyno/ iStockphoto.com, Figure 2.30 © Ules Barnwell/iStockphoto.com, Figure 2.44 © Jaap Hart/iStockphoto.com, Figure 2.47 © BAO-RF – Fotolia.com, Figure 2.49b © Dieter K. Henke/iStockphoto.com, Figure 2.50 © Dallas Powell – Fotolia.com, Figure 2.55 © Oksana Perkins/iStockphoto.com, Figure 2.56 reprinted with kind permission of Smile Plastics, Figure 2.57 reprinted with kind permission of Smile Plastics, Figures 3.51 and 3.52 reprinted with kind permission of Boxford Ltd, Figure 3.105 Maximilian Stock Ltd/Science Photo Library, Figure 3.53 © 36Clicks – Fotolia.com, Figure 3.63 © Oksana Perkins/iStockphoto.com, Figure 3.77 reprinted with kind permission of CR Clarke & Co UK Ltd, Figure 3.83 reprinted with kind permission of CR Clarke & Co UK Ltd, Figure 3.104 reprinted with kind permission of CR Clarke & Co UK Ltd, Figure 3.109 reprinted with kind permission of CR Clarke & Co UK Ltd, Figure 3.110 © jenny-Fotolia.com, Figures 4.1–4.5 reprinted with kind permission of TechSoft UK Ltd, Figure 4.12 © Golkin Oleg/iStockphoto.com, Figure 4.16 © Onur Döngel/iStockphoto.com, Figure 4.17 reprinted with kind permission of TechSoft UK Ltd, Figure 4.18 © Ivonne Wierink – Fotolia.com, Figures 4.19 and 4.20 reprinted with kind permission of TechSoft UK Ltd, Figures 4.21 and 4.22 reprinted with kind permission of Boxford Ltd, Figure 4.24 © Chris Fertnig/iStockphoto.com, Figure 5.1 © J.+W Roth – Fotolia.com, Figure 5.2 Philippe Psaila/Science Photo Library, Figure 5.3 Rosenfeld Images Ltd/Science Photo Library, Figure 5.5 reprinted with kind permission of

Boxford Ltd, Figure 5.7 © Dan Barnes/iStockphoto.com, Figure 7.1 © Elena Elisseeva – Fotolia.com, Figure 7.3 © Chris Elwell/iStockphoto.com, Figure 7.10 © Les Cunliffe – Fotolia.com, Figure 8.7 © Elena Schweitzer/iStockphoto.com, Figure 9.3 © Andrey Prokhorov/iStockphoto.com, Figure 9.4 © Tye Carnelli/iStockphoto.com, Figure 9.5 © Achim Prill/iStockphoto.com, Figure 9.6 © Marcus Clackson/iStockphoto.com, Figure 9.7 © Olivier Blondeau/iStockphoto.com, Figure 9.8 © Gary Unwin – Fotolia.com, Figure 9.9 © Dawn Hudson – Fotolia.com, Figure 9.10 reproduced with permission, Figure 9.11 © Dena Steiner/iStockphoto.com.

All other photos in this volume taken by the authors.

All illustrations by Oxford Designers & Illustrators

HOW TO GET THE MOST OUT OF THIS BOOK

Welcome to OCR Design and Technology for GCSE Resistant Materials (specification numbers J306 and J046).

The book has been designed to support you throughout your GCSE course. It provides clear and precise guidance for each of the four units that make up the full course qualification, along with detailed information about the subject content of the course. It will be an extremely effective resource in helping you prepare for both Controlled Assessment and examined units.

The book has been written and developed by a team of writers who have considerable specialist knowledge of the subject area and are all very experienced teachers.

The book:
- *is student focused. The aim of the book is to help you achieve the best possible results from your study of GCSE Resistant Materials*
- *gives clear guidance of exactly what is expected of you in both Controlled Assessment and examined units*
- *contains examiner tips and guidance to help improve your performance in both Controlled Assessment and examined units*
- *provides detailed information relating to the subject content and designing*
- *is designed to help you locate information quickly*
- *is focused on the OCR specification for GCSE Resistant Materials*
- *has relevance and value to other GCSE Resistant Materials courses*

The book outlines the knowledge, skills and understanding required to be successful within GCSE Resistant Materials. It is designed to give you a 'body of knowledge' which can be used to develop your own knowledge and understanding during the course and support you when undertaking both Controlled Assessment and examined units.

Chapters 1–7 form the 'body of knowledge'. Chapters 8–11 give specific guidance about each of the units that make up the GCSE course.

Unit A561 Introduction to Designing and Making

Chapter 8 gives detailed information about the structure of the Controlled Assessment Unit and the rules relating to the Controlled Assessment task you will undertake. It clearly explains what you need to do section by section and includes examiner tips to help improve your performance. Specific reference is made to the assessment criteria and an explanation is provided as to how the criteria will be applied to your product. Examples of students' work are used within the text to reinforce the requirements of each section.

Unit A562 Sustainable Design

This chapter provides detailed information relating to this unit. It gives a clear explanation of the structure of the examination and gives further information relating to the key aspects of sustainability in relation to GCSE Resistant Materials. The chapter examines:

- the 6 Rs in relation to Resistant Materials
- the social and moral issues linked to the manufacture, use and disposal of products manufactured using Resistant Materials
- the impact of cultural issues on Resistant Materials
- the sustainable use of resources and the influence of sustainability upon material selection
- issues affecting the design of new products.

Unit A563 Making Quality Products

Chapter 10 follows a similar format to Chapter 8. It explains the requirement of the unit section by section and includes examiner tips to guide you through the Controlled Assessment task.

Unit A564 Technical Aspects of Designing and Making

Chapter 11 is designed to help you prepare for the written examination. It clearly describes the format of the examination paper and gives examples of questions. Examiner tips are given to help you identify the type of question and the approach you should take in completing your answer.

Icons used in this book

Introduction boxes provide a short overview of the topics under discussion in the section.

KEY POINTS

- Key Points boxes list key aspects of a topic.

KEY TERM

Key Terms boxes provide definitions of the technical terms used in the section.

LEARNING OUTCOMES

Learning Outcomes boxes highlight the knowledge and understanding you should have developed by the end of the section.

EXAMINER'S TIPS

Examiner's Tips boxes give tips on how to improve performance in both the Controlled Assessment and examined units.

QUESTIONS

Questions boxes provide practice questions to test key areas of the content of the specification.

ACTIVITY

Activity boxes suggest interesting tasks to support, enhance and extend learning opportunities.

CASE STUDY

Case study boxes provide examples of how real-life businesses use the knowledge and skills discussed.

CHAPTER 1

DESIGNING AND PRODUCTION PLANNING

1.1 IDENTIFICATION OF A DESIGN NEED

LEARNING OUTCOMES

By the end of this section you should have developed a knowledge and understanding of:

- contexts and user groups
- design briefs.

The first stage in designing a new product is identifying a real problem that needs to be solved. It is also important to consider who the users of the product will be.

The problems that you are likely to be involved in solving in your GCSE Design and Technology course will usually arise from everyday situations. Describing the situation where there is a need for a product is called the context.

Context

The context is why there is a need for a new product, for example:

(a) You have a large selection of CDs in your bedroom. They are untidy and it is difficult to find the one you want to listen to.

Figure 1.1 CDs left around a bedroom

Figure 1.2 A CD storage system

(b) You keep getting your keys mixed up with the keys that belong to other members of your family and you need some way to tell which keys are yours.

Figure 1.3 Four sets of keys

Figure 1.4 One set of keys is clearly identified

(c) You have a collection of pens and pencils that you take to school, but they keep getting lost in your bag and sometimes they get damaged. You need something to keep them all together and protect them when you are travelling to school and from lesson to lesson.

Figure 1.5 A collection of pens and pencils

Figure 1.6 A container for pens and pencils

(d) When you are sitting on an easy chair, having a cup of coffee, you put your mug on the floor, but it keeps getting knocked over accidentally and it is awkward to keep reaching down every time you want to have a drink.

Figure 1.7 Mugs left on the floor by an easy chair

Figure 1.8 A small oak coffee table

▌ User group

A user group is a description of a group of people who are likely to use the product you are designing. Examples of user groups are:

(a) Teenage boys and girls.

Figure 1.9 A group of teenage boys and girls

(b) Young men leaving home to go to university.

Figure 1.10 A group of 18-year-old men

(c) A newly married couple.

Figure 1.11 A newly married couple

(d) Children between the ages of eight and ten.

Figure 1.12 A group of eight to ten-year-old boys and girls

As you can see from the above examples, it is important that the user group you identify is not too wide. People's needs and preferences about a product will change dramatically from one user group to another. You should also think about the gender of your intended user group. Is it to be designed for male users, female users or both?

QUESTION

This question is based on the theme of mechanical reachers. Figure 1.13 shows a hand-held mechanical reacher.

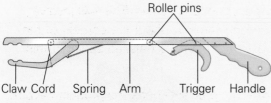

Roller pins

Claw Cord   Spring   Arm   Trigger   Handle

Figure 1.13

Identify two different user groups who might use a hand-held reacher.

▶ The design brief

This is a short statement relating to the context and user group you have identified. It is important that the design brief is worded in such a way that you do not make assumptions about what the product will look like or any other details about the product you might eventually make. So a good design brief would be to 'design and make a product to keep a two-year-old child amused on a long journey'. A poor example of a similar brief would be 'design and make a red toy lorry'.

KEY TERMS

CONTEXT – The situation that has given rise to a product being needed.
USER GROUP – A clearly defined group of people who will be the users of a product.
DESIGN BRIEF – A carefully written, short statement giving the context and user group for a new product.

ACTIVITY

Manufacturers produce children's toys in large quantities. The designer uses a design brief to meet the requirements of the need, the user and the potential market.

In the table below, tick one statement that would be the most suitable design brief for a toy manufacturer.

Design brief	
Design a brightly coloured and safe toy for my own use.	
Design an educational toy suitable for children between the ages of three and five years that could be batch-produced..	
Design a red lorry with wheels, suitable for boys.	
Design and make a toy suitable for young children.	

1.2 ANALYSING A DESIGN BRIEF

By the end of this section you should have developed a knowledge and understanding of:

- how to analyse a design brief by asking and answering a number of key questions.

The short statement given in the design brief does not give sufficient information about the problem you are aiming to resolve by designing a new product. Therefore a full investigation into the problem is needed. This investigation is known as analysing the design brief.

One way of analysing a design brief is to use the **5Ws** method.

(1) Who will use the product?

This may be a particular individual or groups of people and should have been clearly defined in the user group part of the first section. It is important to think carefully about what the people in your user group prefer and what they need from the product.

(2) Where will the product be used?

You need to think carefully about where exactly your product will be used. For example:

- a particular room of the house such as a kitchen or lounge
- a vehicle
- a garden
- a public place such as a park or beach.

Sometimes a product may be for a very specific place, such as for use on a table by the side of a bed or on a desk in an office.

(3) Why is the product needed?

You need to state clearly the problem the product needs to solve. This will involve thinking carefully about the context of the design problem, as detailed earlier in this chapter.

(4) What precisely does the product have to do?

You need to consider carefully exactly what the product has to do. For example, a storage system for DVDs may need to:

- store 50 DVDs
- store DVDs so that the titles can be read easily
- enable each DVD to be placed into the storage system and removed easily
- enable the collection of 50 DVDs to be moved easily from room to room.

(5) When will the product be used?

Some products may be used at particular times or when certain activities are taking place, as in the examples below:

- A lamp may be used for background lighting when a family is watching TV or listening to music.

- A case for a guitar may be used when the musician is travelling to a performance or a rehearsal session.
- A chopping board will be used when salad, vegetables or fruit are being prepared for a meal.
- A parasol may be used when the sun becomes too strong to sit in comfortably on a summer's day.

KEY TERM

THE FIVE Ws – Where and when the product will be used, who will use it, why it will be used and what it will be used for.

1.3 IDENTIFICATION OF COMPLEX ASSOCIATIONS LINKING PRINCIPLES OF GOOD DESIGN AND TECHNOLOGICAL KNOWLEDGE

LEARNING OUTCOMES

By the end of this section you should have developed a knowledge and understanding of:

- the need for technological knowledge as a prerequisite of good design
- the most successful design proposal often being the best compromise between conflicting requirements of size, form, materials, methods of construction and finish.

Producing a design is far from just producing a drawing of a product. Once an idea has been produced it needs to be developed into a final design proposal. This process is all about making decisions about size, form, method of construction, materials and finish.

Developing an initial idea for a product into a final product proposal is a very complex process. The designer needs to have good technological knowledge of materials,

methods of construction and finish. When making a decision about each of these aspects of a design, the designer needs to be aware of the range of possibilities that he or she can choose from, and the advantages and disadvantages each of these possibilities will bring to the product.

Making a decision about one of these aspects is difficult in itself. For example, to make a decision about the material to be used for a component, the designer may need to consider:

- the functional requirements
- economic considerations

- availability
- manufacturing method
- visual properties of the material
- the size and form of the product.

A similar range of considerations can be drawn up for the size and form of the component, the method of construction and the finish. Therefore, making a decision about each of these aspects of a design is a complex process.

Unfortunately, developing a final design proposal is not just about choosing the most promising size and form, material, method of construction and finish for a component in isolation. Some combinations are impossible or undesirable. It would not be possible to manufacture a component from vacuum-formed plywood, for example, as only thermoplastics can be vacuum-formed. All of these decisions need to be considered together. The best design will be the combination of size and form, material, method of construction and finish which offers the best **compromise** between all these aspects of the design.

Figure 1.14 A piece of vacuum-formed thermoplastic

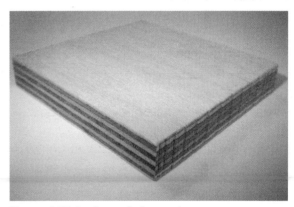

Figure 1.15 A piece of plywood

1.4 RESEARCH, DATA AND ANALYSIS

LEARNING OUTCOMES

By the end of this section you should have developed a knowledge and understanding of:

- methods of gathering information
- different ways of presenting information
- analysing information and drawing conclusions from it
- how to gather useful information by analysing similar products
- the importance of gathering factual information.

Once you have analysed your design brief, you can start researching your project. In this stage of your project you will gather information about what the people in your user group would like and prefer. You will look carefully at products that are already on the market and that do a similar job to the product you are designing.

What do the people in your user group want?

The first piece of research you will need to undertake is to find out exactly what the people in your user group want. This will include:

- establishing exactly what they want the product to do
- any particular features they would like the product to have
- any preferences they may have about the appearance of the product
- information about what the user group

would find acceptable in terms of the life expectancy, maintenance and environmental aspects of the product

- how much your user group would be prepared to pay for the product you are designing
- information about ergonomic considerations which will influence the design of the product.

How to find out what people want

One of the most popular ways of finding out what people want is to design a questionnaire and hand it out for people to complete. It is important only to give out your questionnaire to people who are in the user group you have identified for your product, as asking the wrong people could give you very misleading results.

Conducting an in-depth interview with a small number of people can also give you valuable information about what your user group would like to see in your product. If you are going to conduct interviews you will need to think carefully about the questions you are going to ask and make careful notes about the answers people give.

Looking at existing products

Looking at products which do a similar job to the product you are designing is a very useful source of information and ideas. Look carefully at the similar products you have identified and start by recording factual information about them. This will include:

- cost
- size
- weight
- the materials that have been used
- the methods of construction that have been used
- the finish that has been applied to the product
- features the product has that enable it to do the job for which it was designed
- features that are common to some of the existing products you are looking at
- safety features.

Finding important factual information

It is likely that you will need to find out some essential factual information, particularly when you start to design your product in detail. For example, if you are designing a storage system you must know the size of all the objects you are going to store. It will also be necessary to find factual information about where the product is going to be used. The physical size of the people who are going to use the product will be important too. Anthropometric data will give average sizes of people in your user group that you can use when designing your product.

Presenting research

Try to present as much of the information as possible graphically rather than with lots of writing. The results of surveys and questionnaires are best presented as tables,

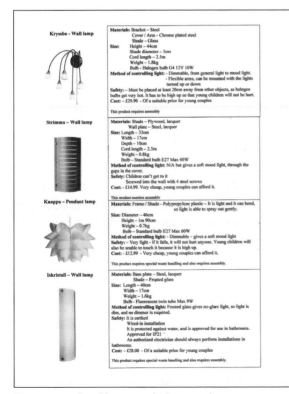

Figure 1.16 Looking at existing products

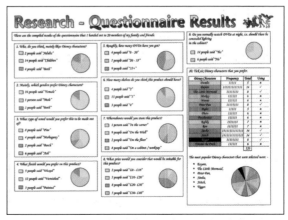

Figure 1.17 Presenting questionnaire results using tables and charts

graphs and charts. Other information can be shown using drawings and notes. The information needs to be displayed so that you can see the results of your research at a glance, as this information will be used to draw up your design specification. It may help you to write your specification if you create a 'summary of research results' page after completing your research activities.

KEY TERMS

EXISTING PRODUCTS – Products which are already being manufactured and sold that do a similar job to the product you are designing.

ANTHROPOMETRIC DATA – Tables of the average measurements of people of a certain age and sex.

1.5 DEVELOPING A DESIGN SPECIFICATION

By the end of this section you should have developed a knowledge and understanding of:

- what a design specification is
- how to write a design specification for a product.

A design specification is a list of requirements which a product must meet. The design specification is written as a result of all the information you have gathered during your research.

A design specification should be written as a list of concise statements in bullet form. Each statement should be as specific as possible, so 'it must weigh less than 400 g' is far better than 'it must be light'.

The design specification will be used as a checklist when deciding which is the best idea from a number of design proposals. It will also form the basis of a number of tests that can be applied to a product when a

prototype has been made and is being evaluated. Specification points can be organised under headings such as 'Essential criteria' and 'Desirable criteria'.

Another way is by writing lists of sentences starting with 'It must…' for the most important requirements, 'It should…' for less important considerations, and then 'It could…' for features that would be an added bonus.

The headings listed below are a useful guide when writing a design specification. Not all of these headings will apply to all products.

Use and performance

This section will list the main purpose of the product, essential features and any other particular requirements of the product. For example, the specification for a CD rack may include the following:

- It must store at least 50 CDs.
- It must store CDs so that the title of each CD is readable.
- It must allow each CD to be stored and removed from the rack easily.

Safety

Safety is one area that cannot be compromised. It is essential that your product complies with all relevant safety standards. In this section it is important that you try to think of all the safety problems that are particularly relevant to your product, such as electrical safety, trapping fingers, sharp edges and so on.

Size

It is likely that you will need to state the maximum or minimum size for a product, and in some cases you may need to state both a maximum and a minimum. Remember, it is much better to say, 'It must be no higher than 300 mm', than, 'It must be as short as possible'.

Weight

The maximum or minimum weight is often important when designing a product. For example, if you are designing a toy for a young child, it would be important that the product is light enough for the child to pick up easily with one hand. A sign to display information in a car park, on the other hand, may have to be fairly heavy so that it does not blow over in the wind.

Appearance

When writing a specification it is important to consider all aspects of appearance, such as shape, colours and textures.

Cost

No matter how good a product is, there is a maximum price that a consumer will pay for it. In most cases it will be sufficient to state the maximum cost of materials. For example, 'It must not cost more than £5.00 for the raw and pre-manufactured materials.'

Expected life

All products will eventually wear out and stop working. How long a product has to last in good working order will have a great influence on the quality of materials, components and manufacturing methods that will need to be used.

Maintenance

Most products will need some form of maintenance from time to time. Products which require less maintenance will be more expensive to make. It may be necessary, therefore, to state in your specification what level of maintenance would be acceptable for the product you are designing.

Environmental requirements

Environmental issues are very important and it may well be necessary to state maximum amounts of certain materials to be used. It may also be necessary to avoid some materials altogether or provide information about how a product can be recycled at the end of its useful life. The manufacturing processes used to produce a product will also be important in what impact a product will have on the environment.

Ergonomics

Ergonomics is about how products interact with people. This interaction takes place through the five senses – sight, sound, smell, taste and touch. You will need to consider each of these and write down any requirements that will be important for the product you are considering.

Specification

Use and Performance
- It must have at least two drawers for storing as much jewellery as possible.
- It must have a tray in the top with separate compartments for keeping the jewellery neatly organized. In the tray it must also have a special place for keeping rings and studded earrings.
- It must be have a lid to keep the jewellery dust free. It must be lined to stop the jewellery getting scratched and damaged.
- It must be able to be uses on a regular basis therefore be of a high quality.
- It must be aesthetically pleasing so that it can be used as a focal point in a young women's bedroom.
- It must be able to store a wide range of jewellery including bracelets, necklaces, rings and earrings.
- It must have a mirror on the inside of the lid so that the women can see what the jewellery looks like and if it matches another item of their jewellery.

Size
- The jewellery box must be large enough to store a wide range of jewellery including bracelets, necklaces, rings and earrings as well as being a focal point in the room however it must not be larger than 20mmx200mmx200mm as this could be a young women's first house so her bedroom could bee small.
- In the jewellery box there must be enough storage space so that a woman would be able to keep all her jewellery in one place.

Weight
- It must not weigh too much as a women might decide to take the jewellery box on holiday or a business trip with her, however it must be strong so that it does not fall over or get knocked off surfaces. Therefore it must be less than 6kg.

Maintenance
- It must take hardly any maintenance as many women will be a work all day so would not have the time to look after it. In addition my user group may have just finished university so still paying of student debts therefore would not have the money to look after it.
- Many women would not purchase a jewellery box that took a lot of money to maintain.

Ergonomics
- It must have no sharp edges.
- It must be appealing to the eye so that young women purchase the product.

Appearance
- It must be aesthetically pleasing and appeal to women aged 21-25.
- It must be a simple design so that it will appeal to more young women.
- It must be made have a pleasant finish (varnish, wax and polish) and not painted one colour.
- It must be of a modern style because otherwise it would not sell to my user group. This includes the handles and the lining. It must have a pattern on the lid and a mirror in the inside of the lid.

Materials
- It must be made from a dark wood, teak, mahogany or walnut.
- It must be lined out of a soft material velvit, leather, felt or cloth. The handles must be strong and attached correctly.

Safety
- It must not have any sharp edges otherwise people would cut themselves.
- The weight needs to be distributed evenly so that it goes not fall over.
- The lid needs to be hinged correctly so that women do not trap their fingers.
- The drawers need to have strong handles so that they can get the drawers out easily.

Durability
- It must stay in good condition for duration of at least 5 years and must stay in good condition throughout this period of time. It must wear well and continue to do its function.

Cost
- It must cost no more than £30 to purchase and no more than £20 in raw materials. This is because many women of this age do not have much money to just finishing university and buying their first home.
- It must cost not much money to maintain as otherwise my user group would buy a different product.

Manufacturing considerations
- It must be able to be produced in bulk.
- It must not waste many materials and must cost no more than £20 in raw materials otherwise the product will be too expensive.

Patent and Copyright laws
- My design must not have already been published because I would be breaking copyright laws or if it has been published I must make sure that it has not been patented because if it has then I need to apply for a copyright of it.

Figure 1.18 A specification for a jewellery container

ACTIVITY

Figure 1.19 shows two different industrially manufactured bedside lights. The lampshades and fittings have been removed.

1. A bedside light must:
   - be electrically safe
   - have a surface finish that would protect it.

Add two more points to the specification.

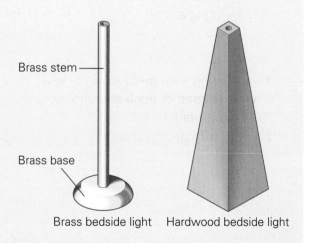

Figure 1.19

2. Figure 1.20 shows an incomplete
   design for a key box to be used in a
   factory. The box is made from steel
   and wall-mounted using the three
   fixing holes.

Fixing holes

   Copy and complete the two
   specifications points for the key box
   and provide a third specification point
   of your own.

   The key box must:

   (a) be made from a strong material
       because _____.

   Figure 1.20

   (b) allow easy access for the keys because _____.

   (c) _____ because _____.

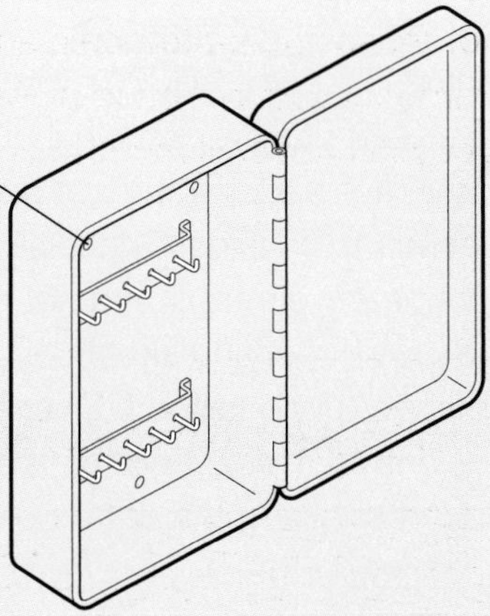

1.6 GENERATING IDEAS AND COMMUNICATING DESIGN

LEARNING OUTCOMES

**By the end of this section you should have developed a
knowledge and understanding of:**

- generating a range of potential solutions
- communicating design ideas clearly through good-quality
  sketching and annotation
- evaluating a range of design ideas, identifying the strengths and
  weaknesses of each and choosing the most promising for further
  development
- the information required on a working drawing.

*After a specification has been written, you can begin to create ideas for a
product to meet the specification you have created for it. These ideas will be
recorded and communicated initially by making sketches for as many ideas as
you can. The most promising ideas will then be developed further into a working
drawing.*

Sketching

Sketching is a good way of recording ideas quickly. Keep drawing simple initial concepts until you have a wide range of possible approaches to consider. Make sure your ideas are completely different and not just variations on one idea. Freehand sketches can be drawn in either two dimensions (2D) or three dimensions (3D). A 2D sketch is a good method of showing the details of an idea. It will show what the product looks like from one particular direction, such as from the top or from the front. A 3D sketch is more difficult to draw, but will give a better idea of how the whole product will look. A 3D sketch will show the top, front and one end of the product.

Always start a sketch with a cuboid just big enough to contain the shape you want to draw, then draw the shape inside the cuboid. This method is called 'crating' and will help you to produce quality 3D sketches of your ideas.

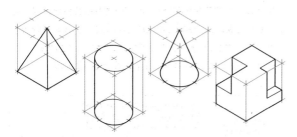

Figure 1.21 Using a cuboid to contain a shape

Shading

Pictorial views are used to give an overall view of an object, but these views will still only be 2D line drawings of a 3D object. Shading is needed to give the object the appearance of being solid. There are a number of ways of achieving this using a wide range of media.

When shading an object it is very important to consider which direction the light is coming from, so that you can work out which surfaces have light falling directly on them and which surfaces will appear darker because they are in shadow. Figure 1.22 shows a rectangular block with light falling on it from the direction shown. The block has been shaded to show a solid appearance.

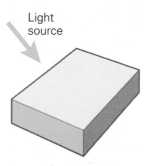

Figure 1.22 A shaded rectangular block

Pencil crayons can be used to produce some excellent results if used with care. The pencil needs to be used at a very low angle so that the side of the lead is used and not the point. Do not put any pressure on the pencil; just use the weight of the pencil itself and keep the shading very light. Just use the slightest hint of colour on the lightest surfaces, with slightly more on surfaces that are in shade.

Figure 1.23 Shading using the side of the pencil

Marker pens can also be used to shade an area. You need to use a pen with a wide chisel point and try not to overlap each stroke of the pen, as overlapped areas will appear darker. It is very difficult to keep sharp edges with a marker pen, so just go over the whole area, then cut out the shape and remount it on a second piece of paper. Marker pens are very useful for representing products made from opaque plastic.

Figure 1.24 Shading using a marker pen

Textures

Adding a texture to a shaded sketch is very useful to indicate the material a product is made from. Wood grain can be added using a darker pencil.

Figure 1.25 Wood grain added with a darker pencil

Metals are very shiny, so to represent metal you need to show the highlights. This is best done by leaving areas with no colour at all or by using a white pencil to draw in highlights over the base colour.

Figure 1.26 Metal is represented by showing the highlights

Adding notes to your sketches

You can draw attention to part of your idea or explain a particular feature by adding notes to your sketches. Make sure you place these around your drawings and not on the drawing itself. Make sure your notes are concise and clearly written.

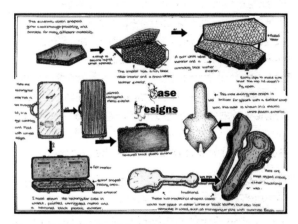

Figure 1.27 Design ideas for a guitar case

Working drawings

You will need to show all the information that is needed to enable your product to be made. It is not important how this information is recorded and communicated, but it will

Figure 1.28 Some aspects of a final design

require a combination of drawings and notes. You will need to show full details of:

- the shape of each component to be made
- the size of each component to be made
- details of the method of construction to be used
- the materials to be used for each component
- details of the finish to be used on each component
- details of any pre-manufactured components
- how all the components fit together.

KEY TERMS

SKETCH – A quickly produced drawing showing some details of a product.
SHADING – Adding colour to a drawing to make it look more solid and three-dimensional.
WORKING DRAWING – The final design drawing from which a product can be made.

ACTIVITY

A school uses a range of hand tools for design and technology activities. Included in this range is a hot glue gun, as shown in figure 1.29.

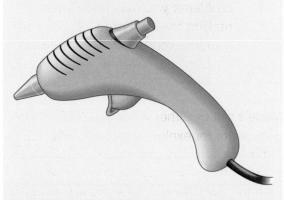

Figure 1.29 A hot glue gun

Using notes and sketches, develop a design for a portable hot glue gun holder. Your design must offer:

(a) stability of storage for the hot glue gun on a bench worktop

(b) safe protection of children from the hot nozzle

(c) a means of containing any nozzle leaks of hot melt glue.

1.7 MODELLING AND TRIALLING TECHNIQUES

LEARNING OUTCOMES

By the end of this section you should have developed a knowledge and understanding of:

- the importance of modelling
- techniques used for 2D and 3D modelling.

Making a model of a design idea is an excellent way of developing an idea into a final design proposal that can be made in resistant materials. Models will allow you to explore lots of the possible problems you may encounter in making the final product. They are also an excellent way of showing how the final product will look.

Figure 1.30 Ideas for lamps modelled from card

Models can be either 2D or 3D. A 2D model is excellent for exploring some details, such as how a mechanism will work. A 3D model is excellent for working out practical details, such as how different parts of the product will be fastened together. Models are normally made using materials that are easy to cut, shape and join. Popular materials for modelling are card, balsa wood and foam. Models can be made to scale or made to the same size as the final product.

Models are very useful as they can be made more quickly and cheaply than making a product in resistant materials.

Paper and card models

Paper and card are commonly used materials because they are available in a range of colours and thicknesses. They are also cheap and easy to cut. They can be joined easily using glue or double-sided tape.

Foam models

Cutting and shaping high-density polystyrene foam is a fast way of creating solid models to make sure that you get the size and shape of your final product right. The foam is supplied

in rectangular blocks which can be cut easily using hand tools and some power tools. The best way of approaching this kind of modelling is to build up the shape you need from smaller individual blocks which can be

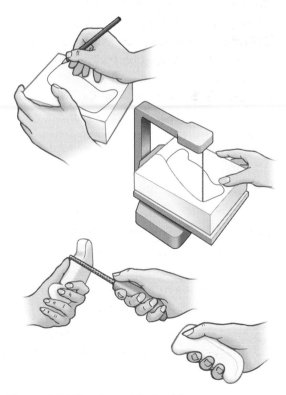

Figure 1.31 Shaping a block of foam

glued together, rather than cutting the shape from a very large single block.

Each piece is first drawn on the block of foam and then cut out using a vibrosaw or bandsaw. Final shaping and finishing can then be carried out using a file and abrasive paper. To colour the model, use acrylic or emulsion paints. When this is dry, further painted detail can be added.

KEY TERM

PRODUCT MODELLING – A representation of a product, produced to enable a product to be visualised, further developed or to solve particular design problems.

1.8 DIGITAL MEDIA AND NEW TECHNOLOGIES

LEARNING OUTCOMES

By the end of this section you should have developed a knowledge and understanding of:

- 2D modelling software
- digital cameras
- use of digital sound and video
- rapid prototyping
- laser cutters.

Digital media and new technologies have developed enormously over the last few years, and designers at all levels have been very quick to use these methods for both designing and making.

Three-dimensional modelling software

Computer software such as Pro/DESKTOP and SolidWorks® is now widely available. These systems allow 3D photorealistic models to be produced. These models can be used to develop design ideas and are a

valuable aid to visualising what a product will look like when it is made. This software is excellent for checking the proportion of a

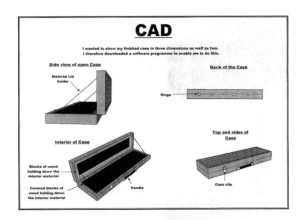

Figure 1.32 A product modelled using 3D modelling software

product or trying out different colour schemes.

Digital cameras

Digital cameras do not use film, so other than the camera itself there is no cost involved in taking a picture with a digital camera. The images they capture can be fed directly into a computer, which is ideal if you are presenting your design folder in an electronic format. If you are presenting your design folder on paper, you will need to print your pictures and mount them onto your design sheets. Digital cameras are ideal for recording research and for recording the stages of making your prototype product in Unit A561 and making your product in Unit A563.

Use of digital sound and video

Short sections of digital sound or video can be used to show many aspects of your design work if you are presenting your work in electronic format. This might include:

- showing how a model or different parts of a model move

- recording the stages of making your prototype product in Unit A561

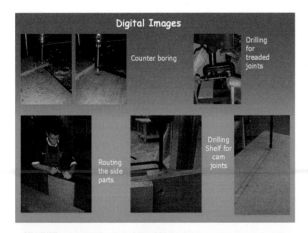

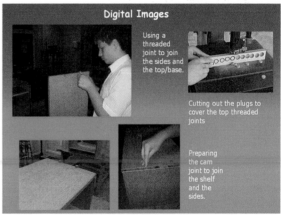

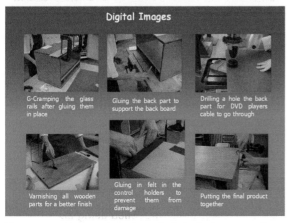

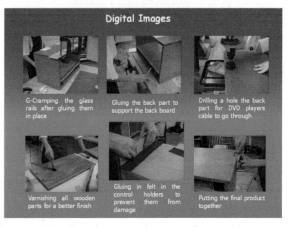

Figures 1.33–1.36 A series of digital photographs and notes showing the manufacture of a product

- recording the stages of making your product in Unit A563
- showing your product in use.

Rapid prototyping

Several systems are now available that enable components to be made directly from designs drawn on a computer. These machines do not cut the component from solid blocks, but build up the shape by solidifying powder or liquids. Computer software is used to slice up the 3D design into a series of layers which are then sent, in order, to the rapid prototyping machine, which builds up the solid component layer by layer.

Figure 1.37 A rapid prototyping machine

Laser cutters

Laser cutters are an excellent way of cutting sheet, card, timber and plastic. They work by vaporising the material along a very narrow line. These machines are very good for making very professional models quickly. Nets made from card can be easily made as the cutter will both score and cut. To use a laser cutter, the design is first drawn using computer-aided design (CAD). Speed and

power settings need to be made on the computer software and the design is then sent to be cut. It is a very easy system to use, particularly as no work holding is needed.

Figure 1.38 A card model and a product cut from acrylic using a laser cutter

Figure 1.39 Nets cut from card with a laser cutter

Laser cutters will also engrave wood, plastic and coated metals, which creates further opportunities to enhance products very easily and to a very high standard.

Figure 1.40 Example of engraving using a laser cutter

KEY TERMS

CAD – Producing a design by drawing on a computer using a software package (computer-aided design).

CAM – Cutting a component for a product by using a machine controlled by a computer (computer-aided manufacturing).

THREE-DIMENSIONAL MODELLING – Producing 3D photorealistic models using computer software.

QUESTIONS

1. Figure 1.41 shows a card model of an adjustable lamp.

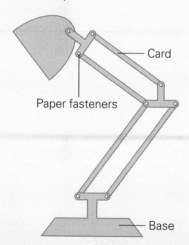

Card

Paper fasteners

Base

Figure 1.41

(a) Give two reasons why making such a model could help in developing the design of the lamp.
(b) State a design factor that this card model cannot tell us about the manufactured lamp when it is in use.

2. Designers use different types of modelling in the design process. Figure 1.42 shows two different models for the design of a wooden bird table.

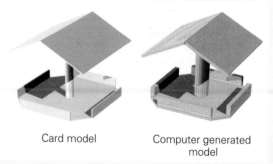

Card model   Computer generated model

Figure 1.42

(a) Give two reasons why designers would use modelling as part of the design process.
(b) Give two advantages of using a card model.
(c) Give two advantages of using a computer-generated model.

1.9 PRODUCTION PLANNING

By the end of this section you should have developed a knowledge and understanding of:

- how to make a stage-by-stage plan for making a product
- the importance of quality assurance and quality control.

When a final design has been completed, the next stage of the design process is planning exactly how the product is to be made. Recording all the stages and the order in which they are to be carried out is called production planning. At this stage you will also have to consider carefully if you will need to make any control devices to help with the production of your product.

Writing a production plan

A good production plan will include a list of the stages of making the product, in order, and the tools and equipment to be used. It will also highlight any safety hazards at each stage and give an estimate of how long each stage will take. It is important to record when quality control checks are needed. This information can be shown using **tables, flow charts** and a **Gantt chart**.

Tables

The best way to start a production plan is to make a list of all the stages needed to make each part of the product you are making and then put them into a table, using the headings shown in table 1.1.

Stage no.	Description of stage	Tools and equipment	Safety	Time
1	Cut 6 mm rod to length	Hacksaw		10 mins
2	Face off in the lathe	Metalwork lathe	Wear goggles No loose clothing	

Table 1.1 A production planning table

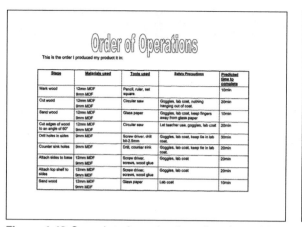

Figure 1.43 Completed production planning tables

Flow charts

The stages of making a component can now be put into a flow chart, and quality control checks can be added where they are needed. Examples of quality control are:

- checking if a piece of material has been cut to the correct length
- checking if a joint fits together properly
- checking if a piece of wood has a smooth surface, after a sanding operation.

Beginning or end   Process   Decision

Figure 1.44 Flow chart symbols

Use ovals to start and end a flow chart, rectangles for descriptions of each stage and diamonds for quality control checks.

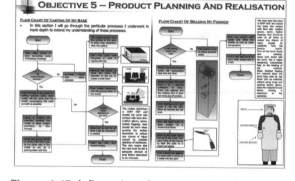

Figure 1.45 A flow chart for production planning

Gantt charts

This is a time plan showing how long each stage of making the product will take and when that stage will be completed. The stages are listed down the left-hand side and timing is plotted across the top. The timing can be plotted in a number of different ways, for example, using dates, weeks, lessons or hours. This chart will show you how long your project will take to make. It can be used while you are making your product to make sure your work will be finished on time.

STAGE	LESSONS										
	1	2	3	4	5	6	7	8	9	10	11
Mark wood to length	■										
Cut wood to length		■									
Mark out joints			▨	▨							
Cut joints					■	■	■				

Table 1.2 A Gantt chart

▶ Quality control and quality assurance

Control devices

Control devices are made to enable one product to be made to a very high standard, or to enable multiple copies of a product to be made quickly and easily. Examples of control devices are:

- a pattern to be used in a vacuum-forming machine
- a pattern from which a sand casting could be made

- a stencil
- a template
- a jig (for drilling, bending, assembly, etc.).

If a control device is needed to enable your product to be made, you will need to plan its manufacture in the same way as outlined previously.

▶ Making a cutting list

Making a full list of all the materials that will be needed to make a product is a very useful part of the planning process. Cutting lists are

QUESTIONS

Figure 1.46 shows a plastic notelet holder. The notelet holder is produced in quantity by injection-moulding.

Quality control is an important part of manufacturing.

Describe two quality control checks that could be carried out during the manufacture of the injection-moulded notelet holder.

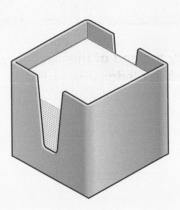

Figure 1.46

Part	No.	Material	Length	Width	Thickness	Diameter
Sides	2	MDF	210	85	8	N/A
Top	1	Plywood	110	85	6	N/A
Base	1	Plywood	130	85	6	N/A
Connecting rods	6	Mild steel	102	N/A	N/A	8

Table 1.3 A completed cutting list

best presented in the form of a table. If you are preparing timber, it is usual to add an extra 10 mm for the length and 5 mm for the width, to allow for final planing and trimming to length. Similarly, when cutting metal rod or similar sections of metal or plastic, 3 mm is usually added to allow for final trimming using a metal turning lathe or other similar techniques. The diameter column is useful for round sections such as metal rod, dowel or plastic tube.

'N/A' for 'not applicable' can be entered in the grid where no measurement needs to be listed.

KEY TERMS

PRODUCTION PLANNING – A step-by-step list of all the stages that need to be carried out to make a product.

CUTTING LIST – A list of all the materials that need to be cut for a product to be made, set out in a table.

QUALITY ASSURANCE – The checks carried out before a product is made and the systems used during manufacture to make sure the product is produced to the required standard.

QUALITY CONTROL – Checks carried out after the product has been made to make sure the product is of the required standard.

1.10 MATERIAL SELECTION

LEARNING OUTCOMES

By the end of this section you should have developed a knowledge and understanding of:

- the requirements that need to be considered when choosing the most suitable material for a component or product.

Many products are made up of a number of different components. Each component has a part to play in making the product do its job properly. You will need to consider each component separately, as one material may be ideal for one part but totally unsuitable for another part.

Functional requirements

Selecting the right material can be very difficult and is often one of the most crucial decisions in determining the success or failure of any product. The final decision is often a case of selecting a material with properties which are the best compromise of a number of conflicting requirements. For example, the best material for a component in terms of its strength may be unsuitable because it is too expensive.

One of the first considerations is the environment in which the product is to be used. Many materials deteriorate very quickly when used outside. MDF and chipboard, for example, are unsuitable for outside use. You also need to consider whether a material will fit in with the environment in which the product is going to be used in terms of its appearance.

The demands which will be made on the material in terms of physical properties such as strength and hardness are another important consideration. Some products need to be made from materials that are good conductors of heat or electricity. Other products may have exactly the opposite requirements and need a material which is a very poor conductor of heat or electricity.

Economics

The cost of a material also needs to be considered, particularly for products that are quite large. Small items such as jewellery require a very small amount of material, so expensive materials like gold, silver and diamonds can be used because of their very attractive appearance.

Availability

Most materials are only available in standard forms of supply, such as rod, sheet, tube, bars or even granules. It will be very expensive or even impossible to obtain a material in any other form, so it is vital to select a material that is readily available in the form you need.

Manufacturing method

Some materials are easy to join together; others may be unsuitable for a particular method of production, such as injection-moulding or vacuum-forming. The scale of production is another consideration in selecting a material.

Visual properties of materials and applied finishes

The material you use for each component will have a major effect on the final appearance of the product. For example, sometimes it will be beneficial to use the natural grain of a piece of solid timber, while for other products the perfectly smooth polished surface of a piece of acrylic sheet may be desirable. The appearance of some materials can be changed by using an applied finish like varnish or paint.

Figure 1.47 The visual properties of materials

1.11 CRITICAL EVALUATION SKILLS

LEARNING OUTCOMES

By the end of this section you should have developed a knowledge and understanding of:

- testing your product
- the importance of other people's views
- recording the changes you have made from your working drawing
- further product development.

The final stage of the design process is to test how well the product does the job it was designed to do. This is done by making an assessment of how well the product performs against each point on the design specification.

Testing

The product needs to be tested by the intended user in its intended location. Ideally, it should be tested in all of the conditions the product will face in its life, including when it is stored and transported, as well as when it is used.

You should devise a series of tests to see how well the product performs against each

of the points on the specification. Some points will be very easy to test – for example, if the specification says 'It must weigh less than 2 kg', the test would be to weigh the product. In this case it will be a definite pass or fail. Other aspects will be much more

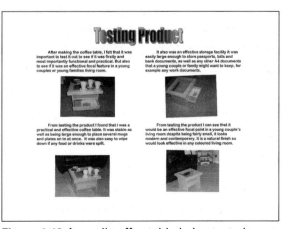

Figure 1.48 A small coffee table being tested

difficult to test – for example, how long the product will last or how easy the product is to use. You will not be able to get a definitive pass or fail; you will only be able to record the opinions.

Gathering other people's views on your product

To gather opinions about your product you will need to let a number of people have direct contact with the product. The most valuable opinions will be from people who:

- are members of the user group for which the product was designed
- have knowledge about similar products
- have qualifications in aspects of the design being evaluated
- have expertise in using the product being evaluated.

You will need to collect these opinions by conducting interviews with people who have used or tested the product, or by getting these people to fill in questionnaires.

You will need to record the results of your testing by:

- video, audio and photography, recording the testing being carried out
- charts and tables showing clearly the results of testing
- charts and tables showing the strengths and weaknesses of the product.

Recording things you have changed after the final design proposal was drawn up

You will need to show any changes you have made to the final product proposal and the reasons why these changes were made. If these are minor modifications, this could be done either by showing alterations to the original working drawings or production plan, or by redrafting these documents.

Improving your finished product

You will need to use sketches, drawings and diagrams, showing possible improvements to the product in the light of the testing and evaluation you have carried out. These could be:

- major changes to the overall design of the product
- minor modifications to individual components
- changes to the materials used
- details of changes to the method of manufacture
- changes to the method of construction
- changes to the finish used.

Figure 1.49 Some details of how a product could be improved

KEY TERM

PRODUCT TESTING – Tests carried out to see how well the product fulfils the design specification.

QUESTIONS

Figure 1.50 shows examples of children's high chairs.

1. In use, rail **X** has been found to be unsatisfactory as a footrest. Sketch a more suitable footrest and show how it is attached to the chair.

2. Describe **two** ways in which the design has considered the safety of the child in high chair **A**.

3. Give **three** reasons why consumers might choose to buy chair **B** in preference to chair **A**.

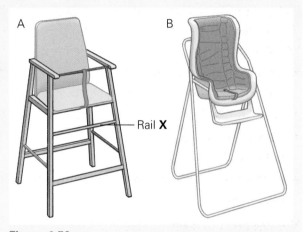

A   B

Rail **X**

Figure 1.50

CHAPTER 2

MATERIALS

By the end of this chapter you should have developed a knowledge and understanding of:

- the general classification of resistant materials
- performance characteristics of resistant materials
- forms of materials and their selection
- the conversion of resistant materials into other usable forms
- the finishing processes applied to resistant materials to improve performance and appearance
- smart and modern materials
- environmental and sustainability issues
- pre-manufactured components.

This chapter deals with a range of resistant materials: wood, metal and plastics. It will help you to undertake design and to carry out controlled assessment tasks and it will prepare you for the written examination elements of the course.

In order to make reasoned decisions about resistant materials, you need to consider different aspects, including information about their uses, properties, availability and environmental issues.

2.1 THE GENERAL CLASSIFICATION OF RESISTANT MATERIALS

Woods

There are two 'families' of solid wood: hardwoods and softwoods.

Hardwoods, such as oak, ash and beech, come from broad-leaved, deciduous trees, that is, trees that shed their leaves in autumn.

Softwoods, such as pine, come from coniferous (cone-bearing) trees that remain evergreen all year round.

Solid wood has a grain that is stronger along its length than across its width. Softwoods generally have a wider grain than hardwoods as they grow faster. Their speed of growth means that softwoods are generally cheaper than hardwoods.

The terms softwood and hardwood are used to describe the cellular structure of the tree. It does not mean that hardwoods are necessarily hard or that softwoods are soft. In fact, balsa wood is a hardwood yet it is light and soft, whereas softwoods like yew are heavy and difficult to work with.

Solid woods contain moisture, and as they dry out they shrink. This can cause the wood to twist, warp and split.

EXAMINER'S TIPS

Examiners ask questions about materials in two ways. They either ask you to name a material or they state a material and ask you why it is suitable – for example, 'Name a suitable hardwood for a child's toy', or 'Give a reason why beech is suitable for a child's toy'.

Name	Source	Properties/working characteristics	Uses
Beech	UK, Europe	Very tough, hard, straight and close-grained; it withstands wear and shocks; polishes well; liable to warp	Chairs, flooring, tools, turnery, toys, steam-bent furniture
Ash	UK, Europe	Wide-grained, tough, very flexible, finishes well	Tool handles, sports equipment including cricket stumps and hockey sticks, ladders
Elm	UK, Europe	Tough, flexible, durable, water-resistant, liable to warp; it can be difficult to work due to its cross-grain	Garden furniture (treated), turnery, interior furniture
Oak	Europe	Heavy, hard, tough, open-grain, finishes well; good outdoors. Due to it containing tannic acid it will corode steel screws, leaving a blue stain	Boat building, floors, gateposts, high-class furniture and fittings
Mahogany	Africa, South America	Easy to work, wide boards available, polishes quite well, but has interlocking grain which makes it difficult to work	Indoor furniture, shop fittings, veneers used to face manufactured boards
Teak	Burma, India	Hard, durable, natural oils resist moisture, fire, acids, alkalis; straight grain, works well; very expensive	Laboratory benches, high-class furniture, veneers, garden furniture, traditional boat decks

Table 2.1 Common hardwoods

Name	Source	Properties/working characteristics	Uses
Redwood (Scots pine)	Northern Europe, Russia	Straight grain, knotty, easy to work, finishes well, durable; widely available and relatively cheap	Most commonly used for construction work; suitable for all inside work but needs protection when used outdoors
Western red cedar	USA, Canada	Lightweight, knot-free, straight grain, contains natural oils that protect from weather, insects, dry rot; fine silky surface	Outdoor joinery, e.g. cladding of buildings, wall panelling
Parana pine	South America	Hard, straight grain, almost knot-free, available in wide boards	Good-quality inside joinery such as staircases and built-in furniture
Whitewood (spruce)	Northern Europe, Canada, USA	Fairly strong, resistant to splitting, easy to work	General indoor furniture

Table 2.2 Common softwoods

Manufactured boards are wood-based materials that are made by compressing and bonding thin sheets of wood, pulp or particles with adhesive.

Advantages of manufactured boards over solid woods

- Manufactured boards are constructed so that they are more stable than solid woods.

- Manufactured boards are available in larger sheet sizes than wood cut directly from trees. Sheets as large as 2440 × 1220 mm can be purchased.

- Manufactured boards are more readily available from do-it-yourself stores and timber merchants than most hardwoods and softwoods.

- Manufactured boards tend to be less expensive than hardwoods and softwoods.

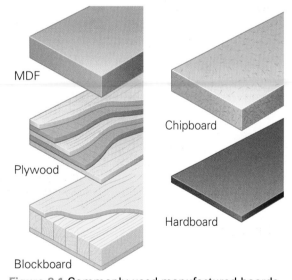

Figure 2.1 Commonly used manufactured boards

MDF

MDF (medium density fibreboard) is made by compressing and gluing tiny particles of wood and fibres together. It has no grain and a very smooth surface. It saws and machines well. It can be painted or covered with veneers. It is used to make indoor furniture.

Plywood

Plywood is made by 'laminating' or gluing together a number of layers known as veneers or plies. Each layer is glued to the previous one with the grain running at 90 degrees. This makes a very stable board that is unlikely to bend, twist or warp. So that the grain of the top and bottom layers of the plywood run in the same direction, there is always an odd number of veneers – three, five, seven and so on. There are different grades of plywood used for specific tasks: marine plywood for boat building; a cheap, coarse grade for concrete 'shuttering' in the building industry; and higher quality plywood used for doors and drawer bottoms in the furniture industry.

Blockboard

Blockboard is made by first gluing together softwood strips side by side, and then sandwiching them between top and bottom veneers or plies. The grain of the plies runs at 90 degrees to the softwood strips. Blockboard is used for furniture such as tabletops.

Chipboard

Chipboard is made by compressing and gluing wooden chips together. Chipboard can be difficult to work with because it tends to crumble. There are different grades for specific tasks: flooring quality or denser quality is used for kitchen surfaces. It is relatively cheap, and although it is not very attractive, it can be purchased covered with a tough veneer or plastic coating to improve its appearance.

Hardboard

Hardboard is made by compressing and gluing small wood fibres together. One side of the board is usually smooth, while the other has a rough texture. Hardboard is used for drawer bottoms and the backs of cabinets. When used for larger items, for example, doors, it needs to be fixed to a wooden frame. It can be used as a cheaper alternative for plywood where strength is not important.

KEY TERMS

HARDWOODS such as oak, ash and beech come from broad-leaved, deciduous trees, that is, trees that shed their leaves in autumn.

SOFTWOODS such as pine come from coniferous (cone-bearing) trees that remain evergreen all year round.

MANUFACTURED BOARDS are wood-based materials that are made by compressing and bonding thin sheets of wood, pulp or particles with adhesive.

▶ Metals

There are two 'families' of metals: ferrous and non-ferrous metals.

Ferrous metals, such as steel, contain iron.

Non-ferrous metals, such as aluminium and copper, do not contain iron.

Ferrous metals contain differing amounts of carbon. The amount of carbon added to the iron depends on the type of steel and the properties required. For example, high-carbon steel, used to make drills, files and chisels, contains much more carbon than mild steel, used to make nuts and bolts.

Both ferrous and non-ferrous metals can be subdivided into two further categories: pure metals and alloys.

Pure metals are made from one single element. Examples include aluminium, copper, iron, lead, tin, zinc, silver and gold.

Alloys are metals that are a mixture of two or more pure metals with other elements to produce a 'tailor-made' metal with special properties not otherwise available in a single metal.

Metal	Composition	Properties/working characteristics	Uses
Cast iron	Remelted pig iron with additions	Hard skin but brittle soft core; rigid under compression but cannot be bent or forged	Heavy crushing machines, car cylinder blocks, machine parts, vices
Mild steel	Alloy of iron and 0.15–0.30% carbon	High tensile strength, ductile, tough, fairly malleable, poor resistance to corrosion; it cannot be hardened due to low carbon content	General purpose, nails, screws, nuts and bolts, plate, sheet, tube, girders, car bodies
Medium-carbon steel	0.30–0.70% carbon	Stronger and harder than mild steel but less ductile, tough and malleable	Garden tools such as trowels and forks, springs
High-carbon steel	0.70–1.40% carbon	Hardest of the carbon steels; less ductile, tough or malleable	Hammers, chisels, screwdrivers, drills, files, taps and dies
Stainless steel	Alloy of steel with 18% chrome and 8% nickel	Resistant to corrosion, hard, tough; difficult to work	Sinks, dishes, cutlery
High-speed steel	Medium-carbon steel with tungsten, chromium, vanadium	Retains hardness at high temperatures; resistant to high level of frictional heat; can only be ground	Drills, lathe cutting tools
High-tensile steel	Low-carbon steel with nickel and chrome	Extremely hard and tough	Gears, shafts, engine parts, turbine blades

Table 2.3 Common ferrous metals

Metal	Composition	Properties/working characteristics	Uses
Aluminium	Pure metal	Light, soft, ductile, malleable, can be welded, good conductor of heat and electricity, corrosion-resistant, polishes well	Aircraft bodies, saucepans, cooking utensils, packaging, foils, cans, window frames
Duralumin	Alloy of aluminium with 4% copper, 1% manganese and magnesium	Equivalent strength as mild steel but much lighter, ductile, machines well, becomes harder when worked	Aircraft and vehicle parts
Copper	Pure metal	Malleable, ductile, tough, good conductor of heat/electricity, easily joined, corrosion-resistant; easily soldered	Electrical wire, hot-water tanks, central-heating pipes, printed circuits
Gilding metal	Alloy of 85% copper, 15% zinc	Corrosion-resistant, solders easily, attractive golden colour; can be enamelled	Beaten metalwork, jewellery
Brass	Alloy of 65% copper, 35% zinc	Corrosion-resistant; heat and electrical conductor, easily joined; casts well	Castings, forgings, ornaments, boat fittings
Bronze	Alloy of 90% copper, 10% tin	Tough, hardwearing, corrosion-resistant	Bearings, castings for statues, coins; air, water and steam valves
Lead	Pure metal	Very soft, heaviest common metal, malleable, corrosion-resistant, low melting point, easy to work	Soft solders, roof coverings, protection against x-ray radiation
Tin	Pure metal	Soft, ductile and malleable, low melting point, corrosion-resistant	Soft solders
Tinplate	Steel sheet coated with tin	Mild steel gives it strength, tin coating bends with the steel; non-toxic	Tin cans, light sheet metalwork
Zinc	Pure metal	Poor strength–weight ratio, low melting point, extremely corrosion-resistant, easily worked	Coating (galvanising) steel, e.g. traditional watering cans, buckets and dustbins, intricate die-castings

Table 2.4 Common non-ferrous metals

KEY TERMS

FERROUS METALS, such as steel, contain iron.

NON-FERROUS METALS, such as aluminium and copper, do not contain iron.

PURE METALS are made from one single element. Examples include aluminium, copper, iron, lead, tin, zinc, silver and gold.

ALLOYS are metals that are a mixture of two or more pure metals with other elements to produce a 'tailor-made' metal with special properties not otherwise available in a single metal.

▶ Plastics

There are two 'families' of plastics.

Thermoplastics, such as acrylic and polythene, can be heated to make them soft so that they can be shaped or formed. When they cool they return to a rigid state. This process can be repeated many times for thermoplastics.

Plastic memory is the ability of thermoplastics to return to their original state after reheating.

Thermosetting plastics, such as melamine, can also be heated to make them soft to shape and form, but this can only be done once. Thermosetting plastics are particularly useful for making products that need to keep their shape and are resistant to heat.

Different plastics products require different working properties. Substances are sometimes added to the raw material used to make a specific plastic. Plasticisers are added to make the plastic very soft and pliable. Dyes and pigments are added to make a particular colour. Fillers are added to increase the 'bulk' of a plastic cheaply.

KEY TERMS

THERMOPLASTICS, such as acrylic and polythene, can be heated to make them soft so that they can be shaped or formed. When they cool they return to a rigid state. This process can be repeated many times for thermoplastics.

PLASTIC MEMORY is the ability of thermoplastics to return to their original state after reheating.

THERMOSETTING PLASTICS, such as melamine, can also be heated to make them soft to shape and form, but this can only be done once. Thermosetting plastics are particularly useful for making products that need to keep their shape and are resistant to heat.

Common name	Properties/working characteristics	Uses
Low-density polythene	Range of colours, tough, flexible, good electrical insulator and chemical resistance	Washing-up liquid, detergent and squeezy bottles, bin liners, carrier bags
High-density polythene	Range of colours, hard, stiff, good chemical resistance, high impact	Milk crates, bottles, pipes, buckets, bowls
PVCu	Stiff, hard, tough, good chemical and weather resistance	Pipes, guttering, roofing sheets, window frames
Polystyrene	Range of colours, stiff, hard, lightweight, safe with food, good water resistance	Disposable plates, cups, fridge linings, model kits, food containers
Expanded polystyrene	Lightweight, absorbs shock, good sound and heat insulator	Sound and heat insulation, protective packaging
Polypropylene	Hard and lightweight, good chemical resistance, can be sterilised, good impact, easily welded together, resistance to work fatigue	Medical equipment, syringes, crates, string, rope, chair shells, containers with integral (built-in) hinges, kitchenware
Nylon	Hard, tough, resilient to wear, self-lubricating, resistant to chemicals and high temperatures	Gear wheels, bearings, curtain-rail fittings, clothing, combs, power-tool cases, hinges
Acrylic	Stiff, hard, clear, durable outdoors, easily machined and polished, good range of colours, excellent impact resistance (glass substitute); does scratch easily	Illuminated signs, aircraft canopies, car rear-light clusters, baths, Perspex™ sheet
ABS	Tough, high-impact strength, lightweight, scratch-resistant, chemical resistance, excellent appearance and finish	Kitchenware, safety helmets, car parts, telephones, food mixers, toys

Table 2.5 Common thermoplastics

Common name	Properties/working characteristics	Uses
Urea-formaldehyde	Stiff, hard, brittle, heat-resistant, good electrical insulator, range of colours	White electrical fittings, domestic appliance parts, wood glue
Melamine-formaldehyde	Stiff, hard, strong, range of colours, scratch- and stain-resistant, odourless	Tableware, decorative laminates for work surfaces, electrical insulation
Phenol-formaldehyde	Stiff, hard, strong, brittle, heat-resistant	Dark electrical fittings, saucepan and kettle handles
Epoxy resin	Good chemical and wear resistance, resists heat to 250 °C, electrical insulator	Adhesive such as Araldite™ used to bond different materials such as wood, metal and porcelain
Polyester resin	When laminated with glass fibre becomes tough, hard and strong; brittle without reinforcement	GRP boats, chair shells, car bodies

Table 2.6 Common thermosetting plastics

 EXAMINER'S TIPS

When naming a material, be specific.

- Do not say 'softwood' when the question demands a specific name, for example, 'western red cedar'.
- Do not say 'metal' when you mean 'mild steel'.
- Do not say 'plastic' when you mean 'polypropylene'.

Examiners will not give a mark for 'strong' or 'strength' as a working property for any material unless it is justified. For example, 'high-impact strength', 'tensile strength' or even 'strong enough to support the weight of...' are all answers that give some justification to 'strong' or 'strength'.

ACTIVITY

1. When you are asked to name a specific material for a product, think of it as a task with four separate stages.

   Stage 1: Ask yourself three questions about the product:
   - What does it do?
   - How is it used?
   - Where is it used?

   Stage 2: Ask yourself:
   What working properties must the material have that is used to make the product?

   Stage 3: Ask yourself:
   Which 'family' of materials would be most suitable: wood, metal and/or plastics?

   Stage 4: Name a suitable, specific material.
   Try this approach for three different products: a wooden garden seat, central heating pipes and the plastic shell for a school chair.

2. Name all the specific materials you can think of that are used in the construction of a mountain bike.

Figure 2.2 Mountain Bike

2.2 PERFORMANCE CHARACTERISTICS OF MATERIALS

The performance characteristics of a material enable it to meet the demands made of it in a particular situation. For example, when deciding which materials are most suitable for making outdoor furniture, you would want to consider those materials that are resistant to moisture or those that are not too heavy, so that the furniture could be moved easily.

EXAMINER'S TIPS

Examiners will be impressed if you can describe a specific performance characteristic from those listed when giving a reason for choosing a material for a particular purpose.

Hardness

Hardness is the extent to which a material will resist cutting and indentations to its surface.

Toughness

Toughness is the extent to which a material can withstand shocks such as hammering. It is the opposite of being brittle.

Strength

Four different types of strength include the ability to withstand being:

- pulled apart or stretched
- crushed or compressed
- twisted
- sheared as a result of a sideways force.

Elasticity

Elasticity is the extent to which a material can be stretched and then return to its original length. Every material has an elastic limit. When a material is stretched further than its limit, its shape is changed permanently.

Flexibility

Flexibility is the ability to bend without breaking and then spring back to its original shape. A material that has no flexibility is rigid.

Impact resistance

Impact resistance is the ability to resist sudden shocks.

Strength-to-weight ratio

The strength-to-weight ratio is a measure of the strength of the material compared to its weight. For example, some materials, such as aluminium, which is a lightweight metal, have a very high strength-to-weight ratio, while others, such as zinc, have a poor strength-to-weight ratio.

Ductility

Ductility is the ability to be stretched like a length of wire without breaking.

Malleability

Malleability is the ability of the material to be hammered, rolled or pressed into shape without breaking.

Thermal and electrical conductivity

Thermal and electrical conductivity is the ability to conduct heat and electricity.

Aesthetic qualities

Aesthetic qualities apply to the physical appearance of the material, for example, colour, grain or surface finish.

ACTIVITY

Using the information in tables 2.1–2.6, draw your own table to carry out the two tasks explained below.

1. For each of the following performance characteristics, name two materials that possess that characteristic.
   - Hardness
   - Toughness
   - Tensile strength
   - Elasticity
   - Flexibility
   - Impact resistance
   - Strength-to-weight ratio
   - Ductility
   - Malleability
   - Thermal and electrical conductivity
   - Aesthetic qualities.

2. Name a different product made from each material.

2.3 FORMS OF MATERIALS AND THEIR SELECTION

▶ Market forms

KEY POINT

- It would be quite possible for materials to be produced in virtually any shape and size we might want, but they are normally made available in standard forms and sizes to cut down production costs.

You need to know about the standard forms and sizes that you can use when designing and making, so that you do not waste time and materials having to make them into different shapes or sizes.

Wood

Figure 2.3 **Market forms**

When a tree is cut down, the branches are cut off and the bark removed from the trunk before it is cut along its length into roughly sawn boards. This is known as **conversion**, and these boards will later be made into the shapes and sizes the wood will be sold in. At this stage we often refer to the wood as **green timber**, meaning that it still contains a lot of moisture, not that it is green in colour.

Green timber is sometimes used for large sections of wood needed for construction, such as the **green oak** frames of some buildings, but normally the timber is dried out, or **seasoned**, before being made into usable forms. This is done by stacking the rough-sawn boards in such a way that air can circulate easily between them and reduce the amount of moisture in the wood. Seasoning can be achieved slowly by allowing the timber to dry out naturally in the air or more quickly by drying the timber in a kiln. Kiln seasoning is more common than air seasoning because it is reliable and easy to control, and also because it produces usable timber more quickly.

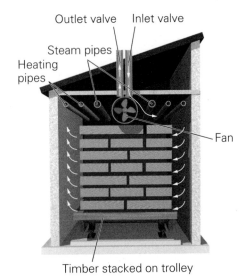

Figure 2.4 **Kiln seasoning timber**

After conversion and seasoning, the timber is ready to be reduced into the standard shapes and sizes it will be sold in. This is carried out using a wide range of woodworking machinery, including circular saws, bandsaws and planing machines.

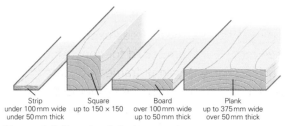

Strip	Square	Board	Plank
under 100 mm wide under 50 mm thick	up to 150 × 150	over 100 mm wide up to 50 mm thick	up to 375 mm wide over 50 mm thick

Figure 2.5 Standard timber sections

Rough-sawn timber is often planed to give a smooth surface to the wood. Planed timber can either be planed on both sides (PBS) or planed all round (PAR), and the planing will make the sizes approximately 3 mm smaller than the (nominal) sawn size. Planed timber is more expensive than sawn timber and is only used where the smooth finish and accurate size is needed.

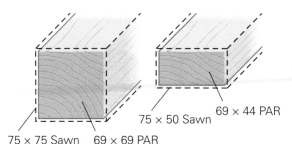

75 × 75 Sawn   69 × 69 PAR

75 × 50 Sawn   69 × 44 PAR

Figure 2.6 Typical planed timber sizes

As well as all these standard sections of timber, it is now possible to buy wood in other forms to suit particular applications. As manufacturing technology improves, the range and number of different forms available is increasing all the time, and in some cases they have been used to replace the original standard forms.

Timber mouldings are available in many different shapes and sizes and can be used for either constructional or decorative purposes. Although they are called mouldings, they are actually made by machining the timber using cutters specially made to produce the shape required, which makes them more expensive than the standard shapes. The wood that is cut away to form the shape of the mouldings is not wasted as it is used in the production of large manufactured boards.

Standard sections

Decorative moulding

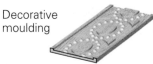

Figure 2.7 Timber mouldings

KEY POINT

- **Manufactured boards** were introduced to cut down on the amount of natural timber being used. They are produced in large sheets and are said to be **stable** as they do not twist and warp like natural timber boards. Much of the material used to make these boards comes from the waste products of timber conversion and machining, making the boards economical as well as useful.

Type of board	Board sizes	Standard thicknesses
MDF	2440 × 1220 mm; 2440 × 607 mm; 1220 × 607 mm	3 mm; 6 mm; 9 mm; 12 mm; 16 mm; 18 mm
Plywood	2440 × 1220 mm	4 mm; 6 mm; 9 mm; 12 mm
Blockboard	2440 × 1220 mm	18 mm
Chipboard	2440 × 1220 mm; 1220 × 607 mm	12 mm; 18 mm
Hardboard	2240 × 1220 mm	3 mm; 6 mm

The smaller board sizes are cut from the standard 2440 × 1220 mm board.
MDF, plywood and chipboard can also be bought with a veneer finish on one or both sides.

Table 2.7 Standard sizes of manufactured boards

Figure 2.8 Manufactured boards

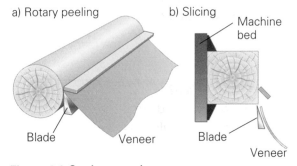

Figure 2.9 Cutting wood veneers

KEY POINT

- Veneers are thin sheets of wood cut from logs by **rotary peeling** on a special lathe or by **slicing** from a long block.

Veneers are used to make plywood and other manufactured boards. Manufactured boards are often covered by veneers to give them a smoother surface and to improve their appearance. A good example of this is the use of expensive hardwood veneers on MDF for making furniture.

KEY TERMS

SEASONING – Drying excess moisture out of newly cut timber.
PAR – Timber that has been 'planed all round'.
MOULDING – Length of shaped section machined from natural timber.
MANUFACTURED BOARD – A sheet of wood-based material mostly made from waste timber products.
VENEER – Thin sheets of natural wood.

ACTIVITY

1. Prepare a stocklist of the wood materials in your workshop. Present this in the form of a table and include details such as name of timber; type of wood (hardwood or softwood); forms and sizes; type and thickness of manufactured boards; shapes of timber mouldings.

2. Visit your local DIY store and look at the timber for sale there.
   (a) How much difference is there between the price of sawn timber and planed timber?
   (b) Why do you think there is this difference?
   (c) How many different shapes of timber mouldings does the store sell?

KEY POINT

- The most commonly used metals can be bought from metal stockholders and suppliers in a range of **standard** shapes and sizes. Producing the metals in these forms is a very time- and energy-consuming process and it would be very expensive to make other shapes and sizes, whereas the standard ones can be bought quite cheaply.

Metals

Figure 2.10 Metals

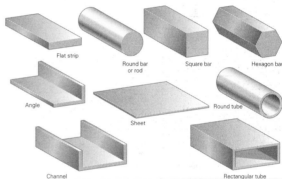

Figure 2.11 Standard metal forms

Because different metals have different uses, not all are made in the full range of forms, so it is important to know what is available for each metal. The metals shown in table 2.8 are ones that you are most likely to use or come across in your project work.

A wide range of sizes is available, but not all metals are made in the full range of sizes, so a metal supplier's stocklist should be used when deciding what size is needed for a particular purpose.

Metal	Wire	Bar	Flat	Tube	Shaped sections
Mild steel		Round Square Hexagon	Strip Sheet Plate	Round Square Rectangular	Angle Channel Tee H section
Aluminium alloy	0.5–3 mm thick	Round Square Hexagon	Strip Sheet Plate	Round Square Rectangular	Angle Channel Tee
Copper	0.5–3 mm thick	Round Square	Strip Sheet	Round	
Brass	0.5–3 mm thick	Round Square Hexagon	Strip Sheet	Round	Angle

Table 2.8 Metal forms commonly available

Sometimes we may need to change our design slightly so that a standard size can be used. For example, if we cannot get 9 mm diameter round bar, we have to decide whether to use 8 or 10 mm instead.

Round and Square Bar	3, 4, 5, 6, 8, 10, 12, 16, 18, 20, 22, 25, 30, 35, 40, 45, 50 mm
Strip	10 × 3, 25 × 3, 50 × 3, 12 × 5, 20 × 5, 50 × 5, 12 × 6, 20 × 6, 50 × 6, 50 × 25, 100 × 50 mm
Sheet	1 m × 1 m, 2 m × 1 m Thickness 0.6, 0.8, 1.0, 1.2, 1.5, 2.0, 2.5, 3.0 mm
Angle	13 × 13 – 3 mm thick, 25 × 25 – 3 mm thick, 25 × 25 – 5 mm thick, 50 × 50 – 6 mm thick

Figure 2.12 Typical standard sizes for mild steel

We also need to consider the cost, because non-ferrous metals are much more expensive than ferrous metals, so we only use them when we need their particular properties.

KEY TERMS

BAR – A length of round, square, hexagonal or octagonal metal.
STRIP – Rectangular sectioned metal.
SHEET – Metal up to 3 mm thick.
TUBE – Hollow metal sections which may be round, square or rectangular.

ACTIVITY

1. **Prepare a stocklist of the metal bar and strip material available in your school workshop. Present the stocklist as a table and give details of: name of metal; type (ferrous or non-ferrous); form (round; square; strip; etc.); size; total length available.**

2. **Compare the amounts of ferrous and non-ferrous metals available in your school workshop. Explain why there may be more of one than the other.**

Figure 2.13 Assortment of standard plastic forms

Plastics

The majority of plastics in common use are **thermoplastics**, which are easily moulded into shape and are also recyclable. The only **thermosetting** plastics we might use in project work are polyester resins for casting or glass-fibre moulding, and epoxy resin adhesives such as Araldite™. Some modern plastics are also **biodegradable**, which means that they will gradually rot away harmlessly after use.

Because plastic is easy to form, it is often cheaper to use than other materials, particularly hardwoods and some non-ferrous metals. It is possible to give plastics the appearance of other materials by the use of colour and texture, and it is sometimes difficult to tell what material something is made from.

KEY POINT

- Plastics are made from natural substances and most modern plastics come from coal or oil. The raw plastic material is produced as powder, granules, pellets and liquid, depending on how it will be used. In many cases, the raw material is moulded directly into shapes required for particular products, but some standard forms are also produced for more general use. Plastic products can be made **self-coloured** by adding colour pigments to the raw material when it is made.

KEY TERM

BIODEGRADABLE – A plastic that breaks down and rots away.

ACTIVITY

Many products are now made from plastics instead of other materials. One example of this is the standard 300 mm ruler, which used to be made from wood.

1. Give two other examples of products made from plastics that have been made from other materials in the past.

2. Draw a labelled sketch of each product and say what advantages there are in making the product from plastic.

Figure 2.14 Overhead electric power cables

▶ Using the right material

Example – electricity supply cables

The metal that conducts electricity best is **gold**, so that might be thought to be the most suitable material for overhead electric cables. That would simply not be possible because of the **cost** and the fact that there is not enough gold available. **Copper** is a very good conductor of electricity and is used for cables in house wiring, but it is too **heavy** to use for large overhead cables because it would sag too much between the pylons. That would mean that the pylons would need to be closer together and many more would be needed, increasing the cost and spoiling the landscape.

Aluminium conducts electricity quite well and is also much lighter and cheaper than copper. Overhead power cables are made from strands of aluminium wire, reinforced with steel to make them less likely to sag. This means that fewer pylons are needed to support the cables and the overall cost of the overhead power line is much lower than it would be if copper were used.

All this means that, when we consider cost and environmental issues, aluminium is the most **suitable** metal to use for the cables,

KEY POINTS

- With so many different materials to choose from, it is often difficult to decide which one to use. It is important that the material for any product is chosen carefully so that we can be sure it is the most suitable one.

- All materials have performance characteristics that make them useful for particular applications, but this does not necessarily mean that they are the most suitable. Other factors have to be considered before we can make sure that we have chosen the right material.

even though it is not the best conductor of electricity.

Example – use of manufactured boards

Figure 2.15 Boarded-up glass door

The broken glass door has been boarded up using a type of laminated board called oriented strand board (OSB), which is made from compressed flakes of wood. This board is strong and cheap but does not look good, so we say it has poor **aesthetic** properties. Because the boarding up is only temporary, the appearance does not matter, and the cost and strength of the board are more important considerations. If the glass in the door were to be replaced permanently with a wooden panel, veneered plywood would be a more suitable material as it would be more aesthetically appealing as well as being strong.

Example – car manufacture

The dashboards of older cars were formed in steel as part of the car's bodywork structure. This meant that they were generally quite plain because of the difficulty of producing difficult shapes in the steel panels.

Modern vehicles have their dashboards formed as plastic mouldings that can be

Figure 2.16 Car dashboards

made into complex and attractive shapes. The use of plastics for dashboards also means that the shapes can be changed easily to suit new car models and design trends. Another important advantage is that less metal is used in the car body, making the vehicle lighter and more fuel-efficient.

ACTIVITY

Give another example of an application where a designer could choose from any one of a number of different materials. List the materials that *could* be used and then decide which one *you* would use. You should present a good sketch of the product or application and give reasons for your choice of material.

2.4 THE CONVERSION OR ALTERING OF MATERIALS INTO OTHER USABLE FORMS

Heat treatment of metals

KEY POINT

- The properties of some metals can be altered to suit particular applications by the use of heat treatment, which involves heating and cooling the metal in a carefully controlled way.

Heat treatment of ferrous metals

Steel is an alloy of iron and carbon, and the amount of carbon it contains governs how tough the material is and how hard it can be made by heat treatment. The structure of the grains in the steel varies according to how much carbon is in the steel and what temperature the steel is heated to. The object of heat treatment processes is to control the structure of the steel to give the properties of hardness, toughness and softness, as required.

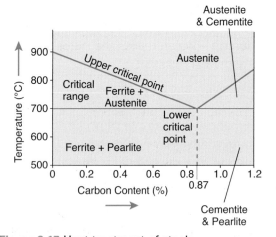

Figure 2.17 Heat treatment of steels

Figure 2.17 shows the structure of steels of different carbon content and the 'critical point' temperatures at which changes take place.

Hardening and tempering

Steels with a carbon content of between 0.8 and 1.4 per cent are called **high-carbon steels** and these can be made hard for use as cutting tools. The process of **hardening** also makes the steel brittle, however, and some of the excess hardness is removed by **tempering** to improve the steel's toughness.

To harden a high-carbon steel, it is heated to a temperature just above the lower critical point to alter its structure. It is then left at that temperature for a short time to 'soak', which allows all of the steel to achieve the correct temperature and structure. The steel is then **quenched** (cooled quickly) in quenching oil or brine (salt water) so that it keeps the hard structure and does not have time to change back. Because the steel is now too hard and brittle to be used, it is **tempered** to remove some of the hardness by heating it to a temperature of 230–300 °C and then quenching again in oil or brine.

In school workshops the temperature of the steel normally has to be judged by eye, and to harden a high-carbon steel chisel it is heated to red-hot before quenching. The end of the chisel is then cleaned with emery cloth to make it clean and bright, before heating it gently until the correct tempering colour appears at the cutting edge. The chisel is

Colour	Temp. °C	Hardness	Typical Uses
Light Straw	230	Hardest	Lathe Tools, Scrapers
Dark Straw	245		Drills, Taps and Dies, Punches
Orange/Brown	260		Hammer heads, Plane irons
Light Purple	270		Scissors, Knives
Dark Purple	280		Saws, Chisels, Axes
Blue	300	Toughest	Springs, Spinners, Vice Jaws

Figure 2.18 Tempering colours and temperatures

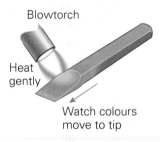

Blowtorch

Heat gently

Watch colours move to tip

Figure 2.19 Tempering a cold chisel

then quenched again to leave a hard cutting edge that will be tough rather than brittle.

When hardening and tempering is carried out in industry, the steel is heated in temperature-controlled furnaces and then transferred mechanically to large quenching tanks, allowing exact control over the whole process.

Steels with less than 0.8 per cent carbon cannot be made as hard as high-carbon steels, and the medium-carbon steels, with 0.4–0.8 per cent carbon, tend to become tougher rather than harder when 'hardened'

by heat treatment. Steels with less than 0.4 per cent carbon are known as mild steels and cannot be hardened in this way at all.

Case hardening

Because mild steel does not contain much carbon, it cannot be hardened in the same way as carbon steels. Case hardening is a process used to give mild steels a hard skin that will resist wear. The whole case-hardening process is made up of two distinct parts: **carburising** – which is the adding of carbon to the outer surface of the steel; and **hardening** – which makes the outer surface hard and wear-resistant.

The carburising can be done by heating the steel to red-hot and then dipping it in carbon powder so that the metal absorbs carbon. This is done two or three times before hardening the metal surface by reheating it to red-hot and quenching in water.

Another way to carburise the surface is to pack the metal in charcoal granules and soak it at a temperature of about 900 °C for a few hours. The metal can then be removed and quenched in the normal way.

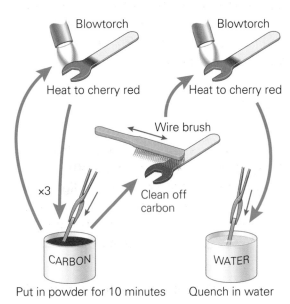

Figure 2.20 **Case hardening a mild steel spanner**

Because there is only a very thin skin of hard metal after case hardening, the centre of the steel remains tough and no tempering is needed.

Annealing

Many metals get harder as work is done to them, which is why some become brittle and break after repeated bending or hammering.

This is called **work hardening** and the annealing process is used to relieve the internal stresses in metal and make it softer and easier to work. It is often used to allow metals to be bent into complex shapes more easily, or to soften the metal after work hardening has taken place

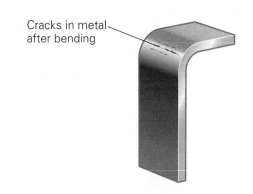

Figure 2.21 **Metal failure after work hardening**

Steel is annealed by heating it to just above the **lower critical point** and allowing it to 'soak' at that temperature for a period of time, depending on its size. The metal then needs to be allowed to cool **as slowly as possible**. The best way to carry out annealing is to use a temperature-controlled furnace, as the metal can be left in it to cool very slowly after it has been switched off. In the school workshop the annealing is usually done on a brazing hearth and the metal is covered with firebricks to stop it cooling too quickly.

Normalising

Normalising is carried out on steel that has become work-hardened by heavy processes such as forging. Unlike annealing, the normalising process does not soften the metal, but makes it tough and ductile by refining the grain structure. Steel is normalised by heating it to just above its **upper critical point** and then allowing it to cool naturally in still air.

Annealing non-ferrous metals

The process of annealing non-ferrous metals is similar to that for steel, but it differs slightly according to the metal being annealed.

Copper is the easiest metal to anneal as it is simply heated to a **dull red heat** and then either quenched in water or left to cool in air.

Brass is also heated to **dull red** for annealing, but it must then be left to cool **slowly**. Brass is said to be '**hot short**', which means it is brittle when red-hot and could crack if quenched in water.

When copper and brass are heated to red-hot, black **scale** forms on the surface of the metal. This scale can be cleaned off by putting the cooled metal in a bath of dilute sulphuric acid (**pickling**) or by rubbing with damp pumice powder and steel wool. If the copper is quenched in water after annealing, the black scale breaks up as the metal contracts, making it easier to clean, but this cannot be done with brass.

Aluminium is rather more difficult to anneal because of its low melting point of around

660 °C; if it were to be overheated it could easily melt. To avoid overheating, the aluminium is first rubbed with soap to act as an indicator when the annealing temperature of 350–400 °C is reached. The metal is then heated gently until the soap turns black and is left to cool naturally.

ACTIVITY

Make two identical cold chisels from tool steel and harden them both. Temper one of the chisels to a light straw colour and quench it. Temper the other chisel to blue before quenching it and then test the two chisels to compare them.

Test 1 – Use both chisels to cut through a piece of 3 mm mild steel held in the vice and see how much damage is done to the cutting edge of the chisel.

Test 2 – Use a file on the end of each chisel and see how much the chisel is marked by six strokes of the file.

Do not forget to wear goggles when carrying out these tests and keep a record of the results. Which of the two chisels do you think would be the best one to use, and why?

Alloying

Most of the alloys we come across are **non-ferrous alloys** that do not contain iron, but one of the most common alloys is **steel**, which is an alloy of iron and carbon and is therefore a **ferrous alloy**.

Examples of ferrous and non-ferrous alloys, their composition, working properties and

KEY TERMS

HARDENING – Heating and quenching steel to make it harder.
QUENCHING – Cooling metal down quickly in oil or water.
TEMPERING – Removing excess hardness and brittleness after hardening.
CASE HARDENING – Hardening the outer skin of mild steel.
WORK HARDENING – Metal getting harder by being hammered or bent.
ANNEALING – Softening metal to make it easier to work.
SOAKING – Keeping metal at a high temperature for a period of time.

KEY POINT

- An **alloy** is a metal compound produced by combining a metal with one or more other elements, often other pure metals. Alloying is used to change the properties of the original metal and make it more useful for other applications.

uses are given in Tables 2.3 and 2.4 on pages 35 and 36.

Composite materials

KEY POINT

- Composite materials are produced by combining different materials to produce better properties. Some composite materials have been around for many years and are now taken for granted, but new composites are constantly being developed as new technologies and discoveries are applied to improve materials.

There are three basic types of composite materials: particle composites, laminate composites and stranded composites.

Particle composites

Particle

Figure 2.22 Particle composite

Concrete is a good example of a particle composite material that has been in use for many years. It is made up of small particles of sand, cement and stone (all ceramic materials) bonded together to give a material with good strength properties. MDF and chipboard are both particle composites as they are made by bonding wood particles with resin adhesives.

More recent particle composites include materials known as **cermets**, which consist of ceramic particles bonded with metal to give strong materials capable of withstanding very high temperatures. The **cemented carbide** tips used on saw blades, milling cutters and lathe tools are typical examples of cermets.

Laminated composites

Laminated

Figure 2.23 Laminated composite

The best example of a laminated composite material is **plywood** because it is very easy to see the laminates, or layers, that make up the material. It is the fact that the layers of wood are bonded together with a resin adhesive that makes plywood a composite material. **Laminated glass** is another good example of a laminated composite, but one that is not so easy to identify. Glass is hard and transparent, but it is not tough and breaks easily. Laminated glass consists of a thin layer of clear plastic sandwiched between two layers of glass to make the material much stronger and safer to use. **Galvanised steel** is a composite material comprised of two metals. The steel is coated with a layer of zinc to give a material that combines the corrosion resistance of zinc with the strength of steel.

Stranded composites

Stranded

Figure 2.24 **Stranded composite**

A common form of stranded composite is glass-reinforced plastic **(GRP)** which is also known as fibreglass. Fine strands (fibres) of glass are embedded in a polyester resin to reinforce it and give the material more strength. A newer and much stronger version of this is known as **carbon fibre**, in which the resin is reinforced by fine strands of carbon. Although expensive, this material is very strong and also light in weight, making it well suited to use in aircraft and some car body applications.

Kevlar™ is the trade name for a very strong, lightweight polymer fibre that is well known for its use in bulletproof clothing. It is five times as strong as steel on a weight-for-weight basis, and it is used as the reinforcement in resin-based composites to produce lightweight structures with great strength.

Figure 2.25 **Examples of carbon fibre and Kevlar™ products**

KEY TERMS

COMPOSITE – A material produced by combining other different materials.
PARTICLE COMPOSITE – Small particles of material bonded by another material.
LAMINATED COMPOSITE – Layers of materials bonded together.
STRANDED COMPOSITE – Strands or fibres bonded in another material.

ACTIVITY

Use the internet to research further examples of composite materials and their uses. Keep a copy of the information about these new materials in your notes.

2.5 THE FINISHING PROCESSES APPLIED TO RESISTANT MATERIALS

▶ Metal finishes

Primers and paints

When painting metal it is important to apply at least three coats: primer, undercoat and top coat.

The primer is applied to the bare metal to help the undercoat and top coat paints to adhere to the metal. An undercoat is applied as the preparation for the final coat. An oil-based gloss finish would be applied finally.

There are traditional oil-based primers and undercoats, but acrylic paints can be used as a single primer and undercoat. The advantage of acrylic paint is that it dries quicker, allowing you to recoat sooner.

Hammerite™ is a 'one-coat' paint, available in a smooth or hammered finish, that gives a quick-drying protective finish for ferrous metals, without the need for a primer or undercoat.

Electroplating

This process enables metals to be protected and their appearance improved by coating their surface with a thin film of metal. The thin film is fused electrically onto the surface. The coating should be less 'reactive' and resistant to chemical attack. Chromium plating is often used to coat car parts, sink and bath taps and cycle parts.

Anodising

Anodising is a process applied to aluminium. The process is similar to electroplating, except that no additional metal is used. Aluminium develops a thin film of oxide that forms a protective layer. This layer can be thickened by anodising. Coloured dyes are often added to provide an attractive metallic surface finish.

Dip-coating

Products that are dip-coated include refrigerator shelves, freezer baskets and tool handles for electrical pliers.

Dip-coating can be carried out in school workshops using polythene in powder form. Polythene is tough and durable. The process is carried out by heating the metal to be coated to 180°C in an oven. The metal is then plunged into a tank of 'fluidised' polythene powder for a few seconds. Fluidisation involves blowing air through the powder in a small tank to make the powder behave like liquid. This way the coating will be applied more evenly to the workpiece. The workpiece is then reheated in an oven to produce a smooth, even finish. Finally, it is left to cool.

Polishing

Items of jewellery made from non-ferrous metals, such as copper, brass, gold and silver, are often polished to allow their natural colour to show through. Depending on the size and shape of the jewellery, polishing can be carried out by hand, using metal polish, or by means of a polishing mop fitted onto the wheel of a buffing machine. Polishing compound is applied to the mop and the workpiece held against the mop as it rotates. A high-quality polished finish can be achieved, but to prevent the polished surface becoming tarnished, a clear lacquer may be applied by means of a brush or spray.

▶ Wood finishes

Varnishes

Polyurethane varnishes give a clear, tough and hard-wearing finish. They provide a plastic coating without actually penetrating the surface of the wood. They are available in matt, satin and gloss finishes. There are coloured varnishes that provide the colour and tough finish in one coat.

Traditional polyurethane varnishes have long drying times, up to eight hours. Recent developments, including quick-drying, water-based polymer varnishes, now mean that you can apply a varnish that dries in 20 minutes and can be recoated in one hour. To achieve a high-quality finish, up to six coats of polyurethane varnish may be applied. A very fine grade of glasspaper should be used to rub down between each coat of varnish.

Marine or 'yacht' varnish has a specific use with products used in water, such as boats.

Primers and paints

The principles of painting wood are the same as those for metal: primer to seal the wood, followed by an undercoat and then a final gloss coat.

Paint is available in many forms. Emulsion paints are suitable for covering large areas such as walls because they are relatively inexpensive and can be applied quickly with a large brush or roller. They are water-based and not very durable. Oil-based paints, including non-drip types, are tough, hard-wearing and weatherproof. Acrylic paints are quick-drying and can be applied straight onto wood or even on top of varnish.

Stains

Stains do not actually protect the wood. Their primary use is to show off the grain and make it look like a different and sometimes more expensive wood; for example, there are light oak and dark oak stains. Bright-coloured stains are sometimes used on children's toys. Stains are not easy to apply and they can be difficult to match, so it is advisable to test them on scrap wood first.

Polishes

There are numerous different clear liquid polishes that can be applied to wood. Clear polish allows the beauty of the wood grain to show through. French polish is a mixture of methylated spirits and shellac and is applied by a cloth rubber (a wad of cotton wool wrapped inside a piece of cloth). There are other similar polishes, including white and button. These polishes are often used to seal the grain before finishing with a wax polish. The important part of the process is to build up each of the layers gradually, making sure that each coat is sanded down before the next one is applied.

Oils

Oils give a natural finish as they help prevent wood from drying out and they replace the wood's natural oil. Teak oil can be applied to teak and iroko, which are oily woods. Olive oil can be applied to kitchenware that will come into contact with food as it is colourless and odourless. Danish oil is made mainly from linseed oil and is excellent for interior and exterior furniture.

Wax

Wax polish can be applied on top of bare wood or wood sealed with French polish. Beeswax is the traditional wax and may be applied to bare wood. The dull gloss shine would result after numerous applications. Silicone wax gives greater protection where hot drinks may be placed.

Preservatives

Whereas varnishes provide protection by adding a plastic coating on top of the surface of the wood, preservatives penetrate deeply into the wood. Wood used outdoors can be affected by fungus, insects or weather. Preservatives are widely available in a variety of colours and are a big improvement on the traditional creosote which was the most common preservative used on sheds and fencing.

EXAMINER'S TIPS

When examination questions ask you to name a suitable finish, your answer needs to be precise. With so many different finishes on the market, you can understand why examiners are unlikely to reward vague answers such as 'paint' or 'varnish'.

Plastics: self-finishing and polishing

Most project work in school involves the use of acrylic sheet. The surface of acrylic plastic is highly polished and shiny. To maintain this finish it is important to keep the backing paper or plastic film on the surface when working the material. The edges of the plastic become rough and scratched when sawn, sanded or filed. To produce the same quality of finish to the edges as the surface, the following processes should be carried out:

- Draw-filing or the use of a scraper will remove deep scratches. (Scrapers can be made from old hacksaw blades.)

- Rub the edges on a sheet of silicon carbide (wet and dry) paper fastened to a board or wrap the paper around a cork block to keep the edges square. Use a medium/coarse grit 150.

- Repeat the process using a finer grit 400.

- Apply an appropriate polishing compound, such as Vonax®, to a soft calico mop and apply the edge of the plastic to it to produce a high-quality finish. It is essential to use the correct mop and polishing compound and to apply the correct pressure. Too hard a mop or too much pressure will heat the

plastic and actually melt the edge you want to appear highly polished.

Surface preparation for the application of a finish

Preparing metal

There are different processes for different metals requiring different finishes. If a bright finish is required for steel, there are a number of important processes to be carried out. It may need to be draw-filed along its length in one direction before it is cleaned with various grades of emery cloth. The grades should vary from coarse to fine, with each grade resulting in finer scratches that will become so fine as to be virtually invisible.

Alternatively, if the steel is to be painted, less attention needs to be placed on the quality of finish as it will be covered. The surface will need to be degreased before applying the paint. This would be done using paraffin or white spirit.

Copper and brass would be pickled in a bath of dilute sulphuric acid to degrease and remove oxides. The metal would be cleaned using pumice powder applied with a damp cloth, then rinsed in water to remove all traces of acid.

Preparing wood

Wood can be planed using a finely set smoothing plane. A cabinet scraper will remove scratches and tears in wood with cross or interlocking grain. Various grades of glasspaper should be used. Wrap the glasspaper around a cork block, so that even pressure can be applied to the wood, and always use the glasspaper along the grain. If you go across the grain, the glasspaper will leave scratches. Start with a medium/fine grade of glasspaper such as F2, and work down to a finer grade 1. It is good practice to wipe off the dust with a damp cloth between applications. On large areas an orbital or belt sander can be used. You will need to take care with a belt sander as they tend to be fierce and need more control. You will still need to work through the different grades of glasspaper when using a machine sander.

▶ The reasons for the use of specific finishes in particular applications

There are three reasons for finishing a product:

- to protect the wood from weathering and the risk of decay
- to protect the wood from minor scratches and abrasions
- to improve the appearance of the surface of the product.

Specific finishes are applied to:

- seal the surface of wood or metal to provide a base for further coats of paint
- insulate from electricity – for example, the handle of electrician's pliers could be plastic-coated
- protect from spillage of liquids or heat from drinks – for example, using polyurethane varnish on the top of a coffee table
- protect from the weather – for example, using wood preservative on outdoor furniture
- make a cheaper wood appear as a more expensive one – for example, using teak wood stain on birch wood

- provide a base metal with protection and a more attractive appearance – for example, electroplating nickel jewellery with silver
- replace natural oils in wood – for example, using olive oil on a cheeseboard
- enhance and improve the appearance – for example, waxing a mahogany cabinet
- prevent tarnishing – for example, using lacquer on copper jewellery
- prevent rusting – for example, galvanising steel.

▶ The application of finishes by means of brush or spray

The main advantages of using a brush are that it is quick and needs no special equipment.

The main advantages of spraying are that it provides a more consistent and even finish.

When using a brush it is important that it is clean before you start, that your brushstrokes are in the same direction and that you clean the brush immediately after use. Oil-based paints and varnishes should be cleaned with white spirit, but acrylic-based paints and emulsions can be cleaned in soap and water.

It is not easy to achieve a high-quality spray finish. Aerosol cans of spray paint are excellent for small jobs, but larger areas may need a spray gun used with a small compressor. Health and safety rules insist on using a well-ventilated area and the wearing of a breathing mask.

QUESTIONS

1. Name an abrasive paper used when preparing or finishing wood, metal and plastics.

2. Name a suitable finish or finishing process for each of the products shown in figures 2.27–2.30.

Figure 2.26 Pair of pliers

Figure 2.27 Bath taps

Figure 2.28 Copper bracelet

Figure 2.29 Outdoor table and chairs

Figure 2.30 Wooden cutting board

2.6 SMART AND MODERN MATERIALS

'Smart' materials react to external changes such as temperature or light and appear to react intelligently. For example, the test strip on drink cans will turn blue when the drink is chilled to the right temperature.

Shape memory alloy

An example of shape memory alloy (SMA) is nitinol, a mixture of nickel and titanium. Although available in many different shapes, its most common use is as wire. SMA works by remembering a shape when heated to a specific temperature. At room temperature the wire can be bent and it will retain this shape, but when heated to the original temperature, the 'transition' temperature, it will return to its original shape. This process can be repeated thousands of times.

SMA wire can be used to move parts of robots and to open or close valves or bolts. Three applications of smart wire are shown in figures 2.31–2.33, providing movement in a straight line, rotary movement and activating a lever on a model of a barrier.

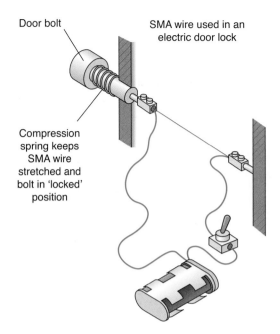

Door bolt

SMA wire used in an electric door lock

Compression spring keeps SMA wire stretched and bolt in 'locked' position

Figure 2.31 Electric door lock

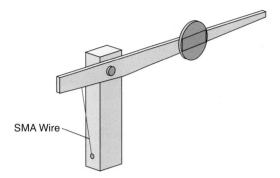

SMA Wire

Figure 2.33 SMA wire used to activate a lever on a model barrier

▶ Shape memory polymers

Many plastics have a 'memory'. The most common that you are likely to have worked with is acrylic. When heated, the plastic becomes pliable and can be shaped. After it has been allowed to cool it can be reheated and it returns to its original shape.

Four stages involved in making an acrylic key fob are shown below.

Stage 1

Heat the acrylic in an oven to soften it. Press the letters 'KEYS' into the surface of the acrylic using a weight or scrap wood and G cramp.

Stage 2

The letters will have made an indentation in the acrylic. Allow the acrylic to cool.

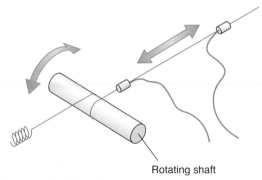

Rotating shaft

Figure 2.32 SMA wire coiled around a drum, shaft or pulley, producing rotary movement

Figure 2.34 An acrylic key fob

Stage 3

File or sand down the acrylic so that the letters 'KEYS' are just visible.

Stage 4

Reheat the acrylic and the letters 'KEYS' will now stand out above the surface of the acrylic. The plastic has remembered its shape.

▶ Polymorph

Polymorph is a thermoplastic supplied in granular form. It is a 'smart' polymer because the granules become soft when immersed in hot water and the plastic can then be moulded by hand to the required shape. By re-immersing the plastic in hot water it can be remoulded. At room temperature, polymorph can be machined and cut in the same way as other plastics. Polymorph is excellent for handles of tools as it can be ergonomically shaped, and since it shrinks as it cools there is no need to glue it onto the tool itself.

1 Granules of polymorph   2 Add hot water   3 Lift out of water when soft

4 Mould to shape

Figure 2.35 The four stages using polymorph

▶ Thermochromic materials

Thermochromic materials change colour at specific temperatures. The material is incorporated into a special ink and then printed onto plastic to produce thermometers or temperature indicators. One popular application is the test strip on the side of a battery (as shown in Figure 2.36). The strip is pressed at each end, and if the battery is in good condition, current flows through a printed resistor under a thermochromic film and heats it, producing a colour change.

Figure 2.36 Battery showing test strip

▶ Thermochromic sheet

This material is a black plastic (self-adhesive) film, coated with thermochromic ink. When heated from its original temperature, the sheet turns bright blue, showing clearly that there has been a change in temperature. The sheet can be cut into any shape and added to products, such as electronic circuitry and food containers, to show when the temperature is too high.

▶ Thermochromic pigments

Thermochromic pigments are supplied in paste form and can be mixed with any type of acrylic paint. When applied to coffee mugs, for example, the colour is visible, but as the hot water is poured into the mug the colour disappears and an image can be seen (see Figures 2.37–2.40). When the temperature falls, the colour returns. It is possible to mix the pigment with acrylic paints of different colours. Other applications for these pigments include kitchenware, baby feeding spoons and drink stirrers.

Figure 2.37

Figure 2.38

Figure 2.39

Figure 2.40

Photochromic materials

Photochromic materials change colour according to the light available. One popular application is spectacles that react to changing light conditions by darkening in bright sunlight. The pigment can be used in exactly the same way as for thermochromic pigment.

ACTIVITY

Think of as many products as you can associated with heat in one form or another and consider how thermochromic materials could be used in their design.

Various modern wood-based and metal-based materials

Many of the developments with traditional materials such as wood and metal do not appear as exciting as the visual impression made by 'smart' materials, but they are very important. Some of the materials described will have practical applications for your projects in design and technology, while some will have more commercial or industrial uses.

Flexiply®

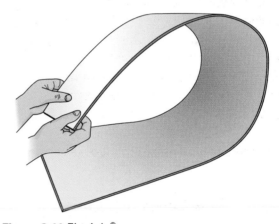

Figure 2.41 Flexiply®

You will already know about plywood and how it is used, but Flexiply® has numerous advantages over traditional plywood. The name tells you about its additional property: the ability to be bent to shape by hand to radii as small as 25 mm. Sheets are available as 2440 × 1220 mm and thicknesses 3 mm, 5 mm, 8 mm and 15 mm. No special equipment is needed to bend it and complex multi-radii shapes can be produced.

ACTIVITY

Think of products that are made from metal or plastic because of their ability to be bent to shape. Which of these could be replaced with Flexiply®?

Flexi-veneer

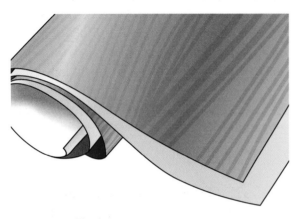

Figure 2.42 Flexi-veneer

If you have ever picked up a sheet of veneer you will know how brittle or delicate it can be and how easily it can split. Flexi-veneer helps to overcome this problem. Flexi-veneer is a paper-backed product 0.8 mm thick, supplied as a roll. Flexi-veneer can be cut using a knife or even a laser cutter.

Hexaboard

Hexaboard is mainly used by industry because of its extreme durability. Hexaboard is a PVC-laminated plywood. Applications include flooring for some commercial aircraft.

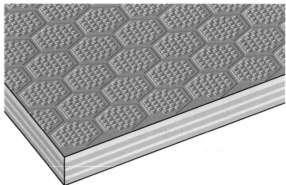

Figure 2.43 Hexaboard

Anodised aluminium sheet

(Anodising is described above under 'Metal finishes' on page 56.) Aluminium can only be anodised on a small scale in a school workshop, so it is useful to know that there is a form of aluminium sheet pre-anodised, ready for use, available in a range of colours and thicknesses. The sheet can be worked using traditional metalworking tools such as saws, drills and punches.

Aluminium composite sheet

This sheet is a composite because it has a polythene core sandwiched between aluminium backing sheets. The backing sheets are available in different colours. It is lightweight, rigid, weather- and corrosion-resistant, retains a high level of flatness, has good thermal insulation and impact resistance. Because of these properties it is used for panelling and fascias on buildings.

Nanotechnology

Nanotechnology is the science of the 'very small'. It is concerned with the control of 'matter' on an atomic and molecular scale. To give you some idea of how small a scale we are talking about, one nanometre is equal to one-millionth of a millimetre.

One example of this technology is carbon. When carbon atoms are arranged in one way, diamonds are produced; arrange them another way and we have graphite for pencils; arrange them randomly and we produce soot.

One exciting development in nanotechnology is the production of carbon nanotubes: with the right arrangement of atoms it is possible to produce a material that is hundreds of times stronger than steel, yet much lighter.

Some of the applications of nanotechnology include tennis racquets, golf clubs and cycle frames, and as coatings for products such as self-cleaning glass and water-repellent wood.

▶ Be aware of other 'smart' and modern materials as they become available

Material science has developed rapidly over the last 30 years and it is impossible to keep pace with all the developments in this field. By the time you are reading this information there are likely to be many more new materials incorporated into the design of everyday products. As an ongoing part of your studies you should keep an open and enquiring mind regarding new materials and try to research the latest articles, whether you have come across them on the television news or on recommended internet websites.

KEY TERM

'SMART' MATERIALS react to external changes such as temperature or light and appear to react intelligently. For example, the test strip on drink cans will turn blue when the drink is chilled to the right temperature.

2.7 ENVIRONMENTAL AND SUSTAINABILITY ISSUES

KEY POINT

- As the worldwide demand for products increases, many of the materials used to make them are quickly running out and, as most are not renewable, there is great concern that this development is not **sustainable**. The extraction and processing of raw materials uses massive amounts of energy and produces atmospheric pollution in the form of **greenhouse gases**. In addition to this, great piles of waste are also produced, causing destruction of wildlife habitat and visual pollution of the environment. Manufacturing uses large amounts of energy and produces much waste and pollution, and the effects of **globalisation** also result in excessive usage of fuel and energy in transporting materials and products around the world.

Figure 2.44 **Environmental effects of manufacturing**

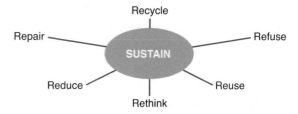

Figure 2.45 **The six Rs of sustainability**

Selection of materials

Designers and manufacturers have a big part to play in improving sustainability and protecting the environment. The design of products should be carefully considered to find ways of reducing the amount of raw material used and increasing the use of more **environmentally friendly** materials. The choice of material to be used for any new product is of great importance, particularly if the product is to be mass-produced.

Advancements in technology and manufacturing processes allow manufacturers to reduce the amount of energy used, and the government's **Environment Act** places legal requirements on industry to control environmental pollution. To help ensure the conservation of materials and the protection of the environment, some basic principles, known as the six Rs, have been developed.

The six Rs

Recycle – Many materials can be recycled and this fact is being used increasingly to great advantage. Using recycled materials not only cuts down the amount of raw material

used, but also reduces the amount of energy needed to process the material. The most common examples of recycling are glass, paper, plastic bottles and metal cans, and all local councils have recycling facilities for these. To help in the sorting and recycling of plastics and metal cans, symbols giving details of the material are printed or embossed on the products during manufacture. It is hoped that, eventually, all plastic and metal used in products will be recyclable.

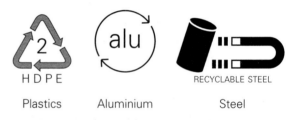

Plastics   Aluminium   Steel

Figure 2.46 **Recycling symbols**

As well as the common examples mentioned above, many other items are also recycled, often on a very large scale. All metals are in high demand, and as the amount of metal ore available decreases, so the cost rises, making recycling vital if metal production is to continue. Aluminium is the best-known example of a recyclable metal as it is so widely publicised. Recycling aluminium consumes 20 times less energy than extracting the metal from its ore (bauxite), and even with the cost of collecting and sorting it is still cost-effective. With millions of aluminium drink cans being used every day, and so much aluminium needed to manufacture products, recycling the metal provides many benefits to manufacturers and also to the environment.

Figure 2.47 Metal for recycling

We do not often consider **wood** to be a recyclable material and, often, waste wood is burnt or sent to landfill, where it biodegrades. Over recent years, more emphasis has been placed on the recycling of waste wood as a means of reducing the overall use of natural timber. By far the biggest user of wood is the construction industry, and much waste is produced in the form of offcuts and timber from the demolition of old buildings. A lot of wood is also used in packaging, particularly for pallets used to transport materials and products around the world. Waste wood is recycled by shredding it into fine particles, mostly for use in the manufacture of chipboard and MDF. Other uses include landscaping products (wood chippings), animal bedding materials and as a renewable fuel source for 'biomass' power stations.

ACTIVITY

Figure 2.48

The tables and benches shown in the photograph have been made from recycled plastic.

Find examples of other products that have been made from recycled wood, metal and plastic, and keep details of the products and materials used in your notes. You will find plenty of information on recycling of materials on the internet.

Reuse – For many years we have been known as a 'throwaway' society and many products have been designed to be **disposable**. Good examples of this are packaging, food containers and drink cups. Although most of these products are made from plastics, they are not normally recycled because of problems with contamination and collection. The 'bag for life' sold by many supermarkets is a good example of a product designed for reuse, particularly as it helps to cut down on the number of plastic carrier bags being used and thrown away. More material is used to produce the bag in the first place, but it will outlast hundreds of carrier bags that can cause damage to the environment and wildlife.

Consumables, including food products, are now often marketed in containers that can be reused by the consumer, either for the same purpose or for something entirely different, like storage or display. Containers can be redesigned to improve their appearance (**aesthetics**) and to encourage people to reuse them.

Reduce – Many products have traditionally been made using much more material than is actually needed. Examples of this are machines that were made using heavy iron castings to make them strong, and wooden beams in buildings that were made from thick sections of timber. In addition to the amount of material used, there is also a great deal of energy used in producing the products in terms of the heat needed to melt the cast iron and the power needed to saw through the thick wood.

Figure 2.49 Milling machine made from iron castings and wooden beams

With raw materials in short supply, we need to reduce the amount of material used by products and this can often be done by redesigning the product, or parts of it. Sometimes the product can be redesigned to be made from a different material that is easier to obtain or recycle, or the structure of the product can be altered so that it uses less material to begin with. Where less material is used, the amount of energy needed to make a product is also reduced. Figure 2.50 shows a moulded plastic connecting block. Instead of making the block strong by using thick sections, a series of 'ribs' has been included in the moulding to stop it buckling during use. The mould for this would be slightly more expensive to make, but with every block made, 80 per cent of the plastic needed for the thicker section would be saved.

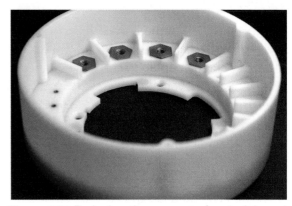

Figure 2.50 Reducing the amount of material used

Refuse – Where materials are in particularly short supply, or the environment is likely to be badly damaged by extracting raw materials, the only solution is to refuse to use the materials. Designers (and, to some extent, manufacturers) have a great influence on sustainability by only specifying materials that are in plentiful supply and whose extraction does not involve the destruction of environmentally sensitive areas. The use of tropical hardwoods, such as teak, has brought about the destruction of large areas of rainforest, further adding to greenhouse gas emissions. In addition, many rainforest trees are ripped out to make way for palm tree plantations in order that the palm oil may be used as a biofuel. Continued use of these materials is not sustainable and alternative materials need to be used to prevent irreversible damage to the environment.

Consumers as well as designers can play their part by **refusing** to buy products that are made from materials that are not sustainable. This could have the effect of causing manufacturers to use other materials, and many companies now advertise their products as having been made using recycled and recyclable materials.

Rethink – There are many ways in which a designer can 'rethink' a product to make it better or more acceptable. Many products are simply 'updated' versions of an existing product, either to improve it or to make it appeal to the consumer more. Changes can be kept to a minimum, at the same time thinking how material and energy usage can be reduced. Often new technologies and processes can be used that will allow the product to be made either with less material or a different material altogether. Sometimes

Figure 2.51 Old and 're-thought' torches

a whole new concept can be applied to the design of the product, such as with the 'wind-up' torch shown in figure 2.51, which uses human rather than electrical energy to charge it. This new concept has meant that fewer 'disposable' batteries are used, and the LEDs that provide the light last much longer than normal bulbs, as well as being brighter.

Repair – In our throwaway society, large numbers of products are disposed of when something goes wrong with them. Many products are sealed units that cannot even be taken apart without destroying the casing, making repair impossible. Because most products are quick to make and quite cheap to buy, it is not considered to be worth spending time or money repairing them, so they are simply thrown away. Not only does this mean that landfill sites fill up more quickly, but also the materials and components used to make the product are wasted, and more material is used to make replacements. A simple redesign of a product's casing could often make repair possible and extend the life of the product considerably.

Life cycle analysis (LCA)

Life cycle analysis is a method used to measure and evaluate the impact of a product across a wide range of environmental issues. LCA involves the collection and analysis of complex data relating to the inputs and outputs of material, energy and all forms of waste. This is carried out over the full life cycle of the product – from raw material extraction and processing, right through to the final end-of-life disposal of the product – and it is often referred to as a 'cradle-to-grave' study.

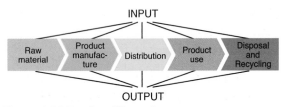

Figure 2.52 Product life cycle

By studying the LCA of a particular product, it is possible to see which stage in the product's life cycle causes most damage to the environment. This will allow a designer to concentrate on that particular aspect when carrying out a redesign of the product. For example, the LCA of a normal family car will show that the most environmental damage is caused during the time of the car's use. This has led to development being carried out to produce more fuel-efficient engines and to find alternative forms of fuel for vehicles. In other cases it may be found that the extraction of the raw material for a product is the most environmentally damaging part of the life cycle, so a designer will consider using a different material for the product.

▶ Design for disassembly

In recent years there has been much concern expressed over environmental issues relating to manufacturing, and regulations have been put in place to ensure control over pollution from industry. It is becoming increasingly obvious that the disposal of products also causes environmental problems, and manufacturers are being forced to become more responsible for the safe disposal and recycling of used products. Governments are gradually passing laws to cover these issues, such as the 'End-of-Life Vehicles' (ELV) and 'Waste Electrical and Electronic Equipment' (WEEE) directives.

The safe disposal of used products involves ensuring that as much material as possible is recycled or reused and that no potentially dangerous substances are allowed to cause pollution to the environment. To make this happen, products need to be easy to take apart and dismantle, and designers are being encouraged to 'design for disassembly'. This often involves changing the construction of a product and the methods used to hold parts in place, but it can also result in the design being simplified and using fewer materials and components. One advantage to the manufacturer is that if a product is designed to be easy to disassemble, it could also be easier to assemble in the first place.

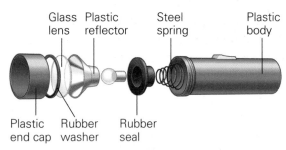

Figure 2.53 Disassembled product

Once the product has been disassembled, all the parts are sorted for either recycling, reuse or safe disposal. Although this may be time-consuming and expensive, if it is done on a large scale, the savings in materials and reused components, together with the environmental benefits, make it economically viable.

▶ Limited product lifetime

Disposable products, such as packaging, single-use razors, carrier bags and food containers, are designed to be used only once and therefore to have a very limited life.

These items are normally more basic in terms of design and quality than other products, and they also use less material.

Many products have been produced using the principle of **planned obsolescence**, meaning that they have been designed to have a limited life and become obsolete after a certain period of time. This principle has been applied to **consumer-durable** products, which have been designed to wear out and need replacing with a new product. Improvements in materials and manufacturing technology have resulted in products lasting much longer than they used to, and many manufacturers are now more concerned with building up **brand loyalty** by producing higher-quality products. Fashion trends and design changes now often limit a product's life, but this is because it becomes less appealing to consumers rather than actually being obsolete, as the product could still be used.

Figure 2.54 'Limited life' products

ACTIVITY

1. The top of the 'mahogany' table in Figure 2.55 has been made from MDF and covered with a thin veneer of natural mahogany.
   (a) Name the six Rs that have been considered in making the tabletop.
   (b) Say how each of the six Rs you have mentioned has been covered in the design and manufacture of the tabletop.
   (c) What benefits are there to the manufacturer in making the tabletop from veneered MDF?

2. Visit your local waste disposal facility and make a list giving details of all the different materials that are collected there separately for recycling. Compare this with facilities provided by other local authorities (councils), using the internet to collect information.

Figure 2.55 'Mahogany' table

KEY TERMS

SUSTAINABLE – Able to continue.
GLOBALISATION – The manufacture of products in different parts of the world.
RECYCLING – Collecting and processing materials so that they can be used again.
DISPOSABLE – Something designed for very limited use.
DURABLE – Something that should last a long time.
OBSOLETE – Unusable or out of date.

CASE STUDY: SMILE PLASTICS

Figure 2.56 Toilet cubicles

Figure 2.57 Reception desk

Smile Plastics is a company that is committed to finding new and innovative ideas and markets for recycled materials, concentrating on transforming plastics waste into multicoloured sheets.

In 1994 the company launched a range of sheets made from shampoo, detergent and milk bottles.

They have since expanded their range of recycled materials to produce plastic sheet made from mobile phones, children's wellington boots, CDs, gas and water pipes, vending machine coffee cups, yoghurt pots and even shredded bank notes.

Recycling is not just one process; it involves a number of processes.

Recycled plastic has to be collected from local authority sites and factories.

There is a wide variety of plastics. The highest-quality recycled plastics contain only one material, so time has to be spent sorting and then cleaning the plastic to remove leftover contents, dirt and labels.

The plastic is then made into 'flakes' or 'small lumps', which are easier to handle.

Smile Plastics buys this material, which looks like

multicoloured cornflakes and, using a process involving heat to fuse the plastic, and a large hydraulic press, the company makes solid sheets of plastic.

The most popular sheet size in their range is 2000 × 1000 mm, but some sheet plastic can be produced as large as 3 × 1.5 m. Thicknesses vary from 3 mm to 25 mm.

The plastic sheets are used for many different purposes, including tables, chairs, garden furniture, kitchen furnishings and surfaces and toilet cubicles.

The plastic sheets have working properties that are very similar to manufactured boards such as MDF. Traditional woodworking tools, including saws and drills, can be used. However, the heat produced by friction when using machine tools can cause the plastic to melt. You may have experienced this when working with thin acrylic sheet. The material can be joined using screws, nuts and bolts and rivets, and thicknesses up to 6 mm can be vacuum formed. The sheet needs no finishing as it has its own semi-gloss finish. Surfaces can be cleaned using mild detergent with warm water.

QUESTIONS

1. Name four tools or machines that could be used to cut or shape recycled plastics.

2. Name three processes that have to take place before Smile Plastics can buy the recycled plastics to make their sheets.

3. Give one benefit to customers when Smile Plastics produces sheet in sizes up to 3 × 1.5 m.

4. Explain why recycled materials are not necessarily cheap to buy.

2.8 PRE-MANUFACTURED STANDARD COMPONENTS

There will be occasions in your school workshop when you will construct and assemble a product, perhaps a wall cabinet, toolbox or coffee table, and need to use a woodscrew, hinge, handle, bracket or knock-down fitting. These are all examples of pre-manufactured standard components. Your design and technology department will stock some essential items, but you may need to visit your local DIY store to buy some of these yourself. This section will look at a whole range of components used in the design and manufacture of everyday products. Because there are thousands of different components, this section includes examples that could be important to both your coursework project and to prepare you for possible examination questions.

▶ Woodscrews

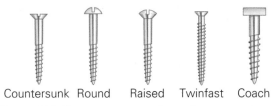

Countersunk   Round   Raised   Twinfast   Coach

Figure 2.58 Common types of woodscrew

Countersunk head

A countersunk head is used when you want the head of the screw to be level with or slightly below the surface, for example, when fitting hinges.

Round head

A round head is used to fasten thin sheet materials such as metal or plastic to wood. The area under the head is able to spread the pressure applied.

Raised head

A raised head is used for decorative purposes, for example, when fitting door furniture such as handles and door plates.

Twinfast

A twinfast is used specifically on chipboard because the coarse thread provides greater holding power.

Coach

A coach is used where great holding power is required, for example, the metalwork vices in your workshop will be fastened to the benches using coach screws. They are tightened with a spanner.

What materials are woodscrews made from?

Woodscrews are made mainly of steel or brass. Since steel screws can rust, some are galvanised (zinc-coated) for outdoor use.

Some are chrome-plated for decorative purposes. Brass screws are softer than steel, so care must be taken when screwing these into hardwoods to avoid them snapping. Some steel screws are painted black, known as 'black-japanned', suitable for outdoor use.

Straight slot   Phillips   Pozidriv

Figure 2.59 Types of screwdriver slots

The main advantage of using Phillips® or Pozidriv® slot screws is that the tip of the screwdriver is less likely to slip out and damage the head of the screw or the surface of the wood.

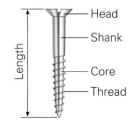

Length — Head

— Shank

— Core

— Thread

Figure 2.60 Parts of a woodscrew

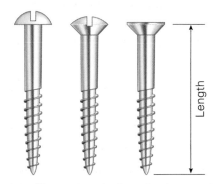

Length

Figure 2.61 Measuring the length of a woodscrew

When choosing woodscrews you will need to answer the following questions:

- How many? (Carpenters and joiners may buy screws in boxes of 200, but smaller packs are available from DIY stores.)
- What type of head? (Phillips, Posidriv or straight.)
- What material? (Steel, brass, galvanised or black-japanned.)
- What length?
- What gauge? (Gauge is the 'thickness' of the woodscrew and is referred to with a number. For example, gauge number 4 is approximately Ø3 mm, 6 is Ø3.5 mm, 8 is Ø4.5 mm and 10 is Ø5 mm. These gauges are the most commonly used and you will notice that they are all even numbers.)

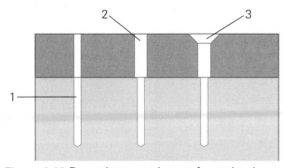

Figure 2.62 **Preparing two pieces of wood to be screwed together with countersunk screws**

When preparing to screw together two pieces of wood with countersunk screws, you should take the following steps, as shown in figure 2.62.

1. Drill a pilot hole to the diameter of the core.
2. Drill a clearance hole slightly larger than the diameter of the shank.
3. Drill the countersunk for the head to 'sit' in.

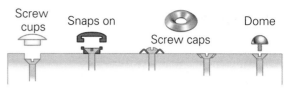

Figure 2.63 **Caps and cups**

There are various types of caps and cups available to push onto, screw into or position under screw heads to improve their appearance. The dome is a particularly good screw-in cap used to screw a mirror to a wall.

Nails

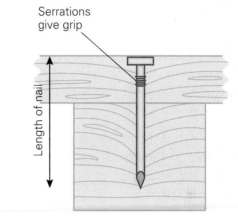

Figure 2.64 **Two pieces of wood fastened with a nail**

Using nails is the quickest way to join pieces of wood. To work, they depend on the friction

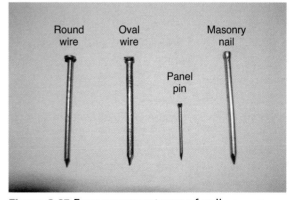

Figure 2.65 **Four common types of nail**

between the sides of the nail and the wood. There are serrations around the shank of a nail that provide extra grip. When buying nails you will need to know the type of nail for the job, the length and the material. Most nails are made from steel, but there are galvanised types as well as brass and copper.

Round wire nails

These are used for general joinery work and range in length from 12 to 150 mm.

Oval wire nails

These are used for interior joinery. Because they have virtually no head, they can be hidden easily and filled. It is important that they are driven into the wood along the grain, otherwise their oval shape could split the wood. They range in length from 12 to 150 mm.

Panel pins

These are used with small-scale work and pinning thin sheet material. They range in length from 12 to 50 mm.

Masonry nails

These are particularly useful if you want to fasten into brickwork or mortar.

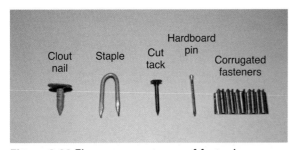

Figure 2.66 Five common types of fastening

Clout nails

These are used specifically to fasten roofing felt to shed roofs. They are galvanised to prevent rusting. They have a wide head to prevent the felt from splitting and give extra wide pressure.

Staples

These are used to make packing crates and in upholstery work. Square types of staple are fired from a gun, whereas the round staple would be hammered into the wood.

Cut tacks

These are used in upholstery to fasten fabric to wooden frames. Because of their appearance they are usually hidden in use.

Hardboard pins

These are used to fasten hardboard to frames. Because of their pointed head they do not need to be punched below the surface of the wood.

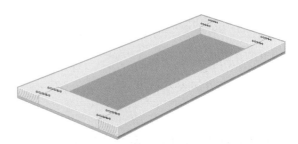

Figure 2.67 Frame shown with corrugated fasteners in each corner

Corrugated fasteners

These are used to make quick, cheap corner joints in wooden frames. They are hammered in across each corner.

Nailing techniques

When you nail a frame together, you should stagger the positions of the nails to avoid splitting the wood along the grain.

Figure 2.68 Staggered nailing

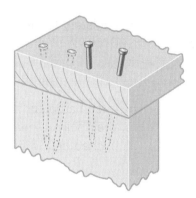

Figure 2.69 Dovetail nailing

Hammering nails into the wood at a slight angle, or 'dovetailed', will make the joint stronger and more difficult to pull apart.

▶ Nuts, bolts and machine screws

These are used to make temporary joints because they can be taken apart using a screwdriver, spanner or Allen key.

Bolts

Bolts are made from high-tensile steel; they have either square or hexagonal heads. They are ordered by the diameter of the thread and their length is measured from underneath the head of the bolt. Some bolts have the thread along their whole length. You can exert great force when tightening bolts with a spanner.

Figure 2.70 Drawing of a hexagonal head bolt

Nuts

Wing nut | Hexagonal nut | Square nut | Locking nut | Castle nut and split pin | Nylon (fibre lock) nut

Figure 2.71 Six types of nut

Nuts have the same types of head as bolts, but wing nuts are specially shaped to be finger-tightened. Lock nuts are designed to prevent loosening of the joint caused by vibration. The castle nut is used in those situations where there is no possibility of the nut coming off as a result of vibration. They are used on cars to tighten wheel bearings.

Machine screws

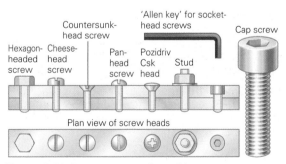

Figure 2.72 Seven types of machine screw

Machine screws are available in a variety of lengths, diameters and types of head. Most can be tightened using a screwdriver, but socket-head machine screws need an Allen key. Allen keys give a very positive fit when tightening the screw, and considerable force can be applied without the danger of the tool slipping out.

Self-tapping screws

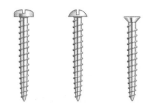

Figure 2.73 Three types of self-tapping screw

Self-tapping screws are made from hardened steel and they cut their own thread as they are screwed into thin sheet material such as metal or plastic. Common sizes are 6 to 50 mm. They can have straight, Phillips® or Posidriv® slots.

Washers

Plain washer | Lock washer | Grover spring washer | Spring washer | Tab washer | Serrated washer

Figure 2.74 Six types of washer

The purpose of a washer is to protect the surface on which the bolt or nut is being tightened, to spread the load and prevent the fixing from vibrating loose.

▶ Knock-down fittings

Knock-down (KD) fittings are used in the construction of furniture. Be careful not to consider flat-pack designed furniture with only KD fittings. While many items of flat-pack do use KD fittings, they also use permanent joints for self-assembly, such as dowel, and supply glue for the consumer to assemble the item. Many of the KD fittings include the use of dowel or metal pins to locate part of the joint. Most of the KD fittings can be fitted using basic tools such as a drill, hammer, mallet and

screwdriver. This is a definite advantage for the consumer. There is a wide variety of KD fittings used in the manufacture of furniture, some of which are available at DIY stores.

One-piece and two-piece corner blocks

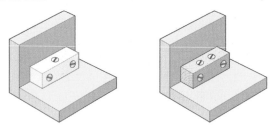

Figure 2.75 One-piece plastic corner block and one-piece wooden corner block

One-piece corner blocks made from plastic are used to join the sides of a cabinet. You could make your own from wood. Remember to use countersunk screws.

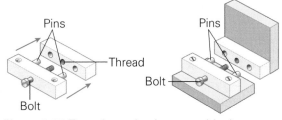

Figure 2.76 Two-piece plastic corner block

A single-threaded bolt fastens one part to the other, while two pins help to locate the two parts. The left-hand part is screwed to the inside of the cabinet.

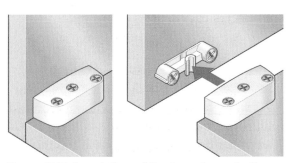

Figure 2.77 A variation of the two-piece plastic corner block

Figure 2.77 shows another type of two-piece fitting. Both parts are screwed against the inside of the cabinet and a final screw is inserted on top of the fitting to keep it in place.

Rigid joint

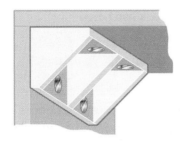

Figure 2.78 Rigid joint

A rigid joint is made from a single piece of moulded plastic, and four screws are used to hold the joint in place.

Scan fittings

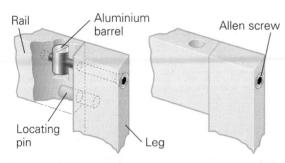

Figure 2.79 Scan fitting

Scan fittings can be used to join frames or the sides of cabinets together. A hole is drilled through the leg into the end of the rail. The aluminium barrel is dropped into a hole drilled into the top of the rail. The aluminium barrel has a threaded hole for the Allen screw to screw into and pull the joint together. A metal locating pin helps to align the two parts.

Cam lock

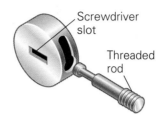
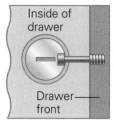

Figure 2.80 Cam lock

One very common use for cam locks is to fasten a drawer front to the sides of the drawer. A threaded rod is screwed into the inside of the drawer front. The circular cam lock is dropped into a drilled hole in the drawer side. A screwdriver is used to turn the cam lock, which then pulls the drawer front towards it, tightening the joint. This is a particularly clever mechanical joint using the principle of the cam.

Leg fastenings

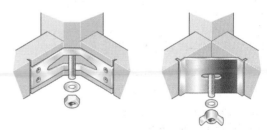

Figure 2.81 Two variations of a leg fastening

It can be particularly useful to be able to take the legs apart from the rest of the table for storage purposes. While the shape of the connecting steel plate is different, the principle is the same. A rod has a woodscrew thread on one end to fit into the leg of the table. On the other end is a screw thread onto which a nut can be tightened.

▶ Hinges

Butt hinge

Butt hinges are one of the most commonly used hinges. They are used for doors, windows and large and small boxes. They are usually recessed into the edge of the wood so that they look very neat. They are commonly made from steel or brass. Fitting a hinge into the edge of a small jewellery box or cabinet takes a lot of care and skill to achieve a high level of appearance.

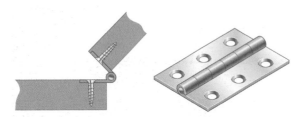

Figure 2.82 Butt hinge

Figure 2.83

Back-flap hinge

Back-flap hinges are used for flaps or 'leaves' on tables or for large lids on boxes. The greater surface area and the spaced holes provide greater strength. In addition, the position of the holes makes it less likely to split the grain, which can happen with butt hinges where the screw holes are all in line.

Figure 2.84 Back-flap hinge

Piano hinge

The name gives a clue to their use. Piano hinges are used where you need a lot of support along the edges of a long product. A case for a snooker cue might use a piano hinge.

Figure 2.85 Piano hinge

Tee hinge

Tee hinges are used on gates and sheds. The long arm with staggered holes would be fastened to the door and give it great support. They are black-japanned (galvanised) to prevent rusting.

Figure 2.86 Tee hinge

Figure 2.87

Flush hinge

These hinges are popular with students because they require no recessing. They are surface-mounted and one flap fits inside the other when closed.

Figure 2.88 Flush hinge

Adjustable concealed hinge

Manufacturers of kitchen cabinets often use adjustable concealed hinges. These hinges give consumers the opportunity to adjust a cabinet door up and down and in and out, simply by loosening and/or tightening particular screws in the hinge itself.

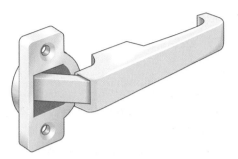

Figure 2.89 Adjustable concealed hinge

Figure 2.90

Stays

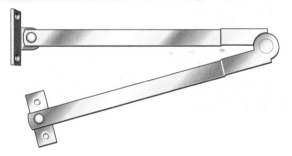

Figure 2.91 Brass stay

Stays are a type of hinge in as much as they connect two parts of a cabinet, for example, and allow the 'fall' on the cabinet to open and close. Good-quality stays are made from solid drawn brass. There are lots of different types of stay, but they all have to screw against the

Figure 2.92 Brass stay with adjustment

inside of the cabinet and to the 'fall'. The stay in figure 2.92 has adjustable resistance, that is, it can be made to fall (open) with little force or needing increased force.

▌ Catches

There are three main types of catch used to keep closed lids on boxes or doors on cabinets: ball, spring and magnetic. They are available in a variety of materials, including brass and plastic, depending on the type of product to which they will be fitted.

Ball catch

Figure 2.93 Ball catch

These are neat and can be recessed so that they are hardly noticeable. They are available

in very small sizes for small-scale cabinet work, or a much larger ball catch can be used to close a door positively.

Spring catch

Figure 2.94 Spring catch

These give a very positive fastening, but tend to be less attractive in appearance and therefore are used for more functional products.

Magnetic catch

Figure 2.95 Magnetic catch

These are available in a variety of materials. Some are made from brass when used on quality cabinet work, while others are made from white plastic, more suitable for kitchen cabinets.

▌ Drawer and door runners

This could be designed and made by a student for their coursework project. The drawer will 'run' inside the cabinet. There are several ways of supporting the drawer. You

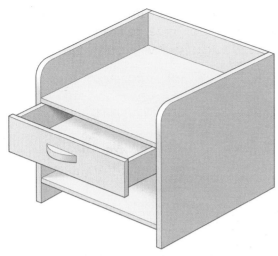

Figure 2.96 Bedside cabinet made from veneered chipboard and sold as flat-pack for self-assembly

could put a shelf inside, but this would use more materials and increase the weight and cost.

Figure 2.97 Drawer inside cabinet

One good way of supporting the drawer is to produce a groove in the side of the drawer and add a strip to the inside of the cabinet. The strip could be pinned and glued in position.

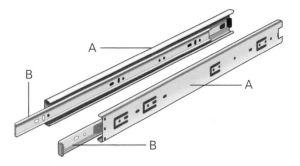

Figure 2.98 Drawer runners

Another way is to buy a pair of drawer runners, as shown in figure 2.98. Parts **A** are screwed to the inside of the cabinet, while parts **B** are screwed to the outside of the drawer. They operate by part **B** sliding in and out of **A**. There are different lengths and types of runners and some would be screwed underneath the drawer.

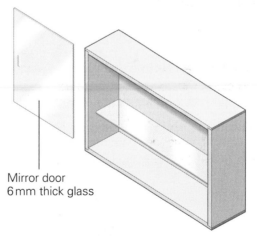

Mirror door
6 mm thick glass

Figure 2.99 Bathroom cabinet made from solid wood with two glass sliding doors and adjustable shelf

With glass sliding doors, the cabinet must be assembled first and then the doors fitted. You must make sure that the doors can be removed for cleaning or replacement if they break. There are three ways of doing this.

Figure 2.101 **Plastic runners**

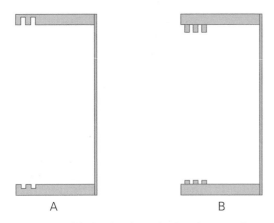

| A | B |

Figure 2.100 Methods of producing 'runners'

In cabinet **A** you could cut two grooves in the bottom and two grooves in the top of the cabinet. In cabinet **B** you could add three strips to the top and bottom to make the grooves. Remember, the grooves in the top must be twice as deep as the grooves in the bottom, so that you can lift them up into the groove.

The third way is to buy lengths of plastic 'channelling' from a DIY store. These can be glued in position.

Drawer and cabinet handles

When you make a cabinet with either a drawer or a small door, you will need some type of handle or 'pull' so that you can open and close them easily. Many students enjoy making their own handles to match their product, but there are hundreds of different types available, either at DIY stores or through mail-order hardware catalogues. There is a vast range of materials, finishes and styles. The advantage of buying a special handle is that it can give your work a really professional finish.

Beech   Polished brass   Anodised aluminium   Oak   Chromed finish

Figure 2.102 Drawer/cabinet handles

▌ Locks

There are many different locks available for a wide range of purposes. Some of these are technically 'catches', used to fasten rather than lock. You will have seen these used on doors, drawers, toolboxes and wooden cases.

Hasp and staple

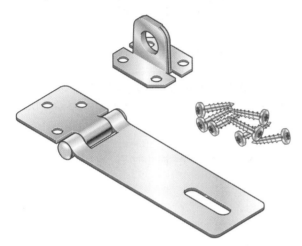

Figure 2.103 **Hasp and staple**

This would be used with a padlock to fasten a shed door or gate for security.

Toggle catch

Figure 2.104 **Toggle catch**

Although these cannot be locked, they can be used to fasten the top and bottom parts of a toolbox or similar case together.

Box-style cupboard catch

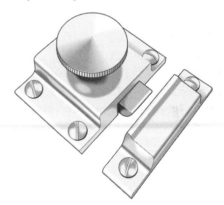

Figure 2.105 **Box-style cupboard catch**

There are many variations of this type of catch used on cabinets and cupboards.

ACTIVITY

1. Look at the cabinet shown in figure 2.106.

   Name and sketch a pre-manufactured component that could be used in the following situations:

   (A) to hold the door closed against the cabinet
   (B) to provide a moving joint between the door and the inside of the cabinet so that the door can remain horizontal when open
   (C) to provide a moving joint between the door and the cabinet
   (D) a KD fitting to join the sides of the cabinet
   (E) a component that allows you to open or close the door
   (F) a component that supports the adjustable shelf.

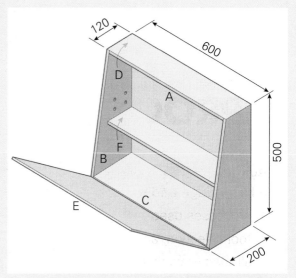

Figure 2.106 Cabinet requiring six different pre-manufactured components

2. Read the information about knock-down fittings, hinges, catches and so on. Look at the furniture you have at home and see how many of the pre-manufactured components we have discussed in this section are used in their manufacture.

CHAPTER 3

TOOLS, EQUIPMENT AND PROCESSES

LEARNING OUTCOMES

By the end of this chapter you should have developed a knowledge and understanding of:

- processes used in product manufacture
- tool selection, and effective and safe use
- alternative tools and equipment that can be used for the same task
- safety checks to be carried out on electrical equipment before use
- the correct settings on machines.

This chapter deals with a wide range of processes that you will need to know about when making products from resistant materials. You will need to be able to identify specific tools or equipment for a particular purpose. Your teacher will show you how to use them properly and safely. Written examinations include questions about these tools and equipment.

3.1 PROCESSES USED IN PRODUCT MANUFACTURE

Preparing, marking out, measuring and testing

The tools and equipment discussed in this section are designed to be used specifically with wood, metal or plastics. However, some can be used with wood and metal, or metal and plastic, or wood and plastic. It is important to be able to identify the correct tools or equipment for the material that you are working with.

Datum faces

Datum faces are sides, edges or ends of material that are perfectly flat and are used to measure or mark out from. Without a flat surface to work from, all your measurements will be inaccurate.

Steel rule

This is used to measure and also to test for flatness.

Marking knife

This is used to mark lines across the grain of wood. The knife cuts the fibres of the wood; it is thinner than a pencil mark and can act as a guide when sawing.

Scriber

The scriber is used to mark out lines on metal or on plastic. It is important that the lines marked on plastic are sawn down or hidden as they cannot be removed.

Chinagraph pencil

This is used to mark out on plastic as it can be rubbed out easily if a mistake is made. Sometimes a non-permanent felt-tip marker is just as good.

Try square

The try square can be used on wood, metal and plastic to mark a line at 90 degrees to an edge. It can also be used to test how square an edge is. Woodworkers' try squares have a wooden stock and a carbon steel blade, while engineers' squares are made entirely from carbon steel.

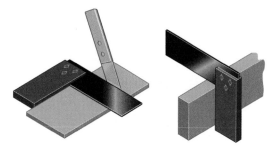

Figure 3.1 Try square

Marking gauge

This is used on wood to draw a line along the grain, parallel to an edge.

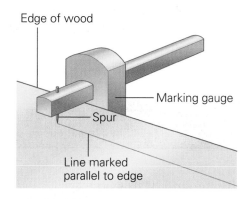

Figure 3.2 Marking gauge

Cutting gauge

This is used on wood to draw a line across the grain, parallel to an end. The difference between a marking gauge and a cutting gauge is that the marking gauge has a spur that makes the mark, while the cutting gauge has a small blade to cut across the fibres of the wood.

Mortise gauge

The mortise gauge is used in the same way as the marking gauge, but it has two spurs that can be adjusted to the required width of the mortise or tenon to be marked out.

Odd-leg calipers

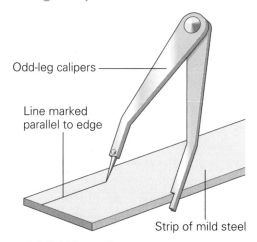

Figure 3.3 Odd-leg calipers

These can be used on metal or plastic to draw a line along the length of the material, parallel to an edge.

Mitre square

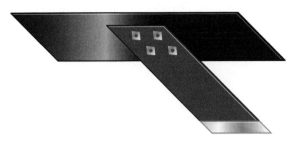

Figure 3.4 Mitre square

The mitre square can be used on wood or plastic to mark out or test angles of 45° or 135°.

Sliding bevel

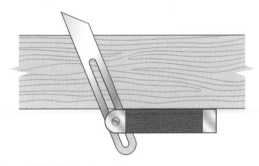

Figure 3.5 Sliding bevel

This can be used on wood, metal or plastic. The blade can be set to any angle, using a protractor, and tightened in position.

Inside and outside calipers

Inside calipers are used to measure the inside diameters of tube. Outside calipers are used to measure the outside diameters of tube or bar.

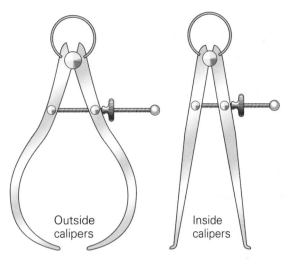

Outside calipers

Inside calipers

Figure 3.6 Inside and outside calipers

ACTIVITY

Ask your teacher if you could have some short ends of a variety of tube and bar. Use the inside and outside calipers to measure their diameters.

Centre square

Figure 3.7 Centre square

This is used to find the centre on round bar. If you draw two lines across the end of the bar using the centre square, where the lines bisect is the centre.

Combination square

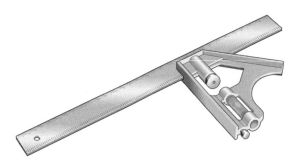

Figure 3.8 Combination square

As its name suggests, this tool will perform a variety of tasks, including measuring like a rule, measuring angles and depths, and checking for squareness over edges.

Centre and dot punches

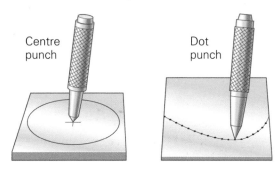

Centre punch

Dot punch

Figure 3.9 Centre and dot punches

These punches are used on metal and plastic. The centre punch is used to mark the centre of the hole to be drilled, while a dot punch is used to mark the centres of circles and arcs that will be marked out. The dot punch is also used to highlight lines to be cut.

Dividers

Figure 3.10 Dividers

Dividers can be used to mark circles and arcs on metal and plastic.

Micrometers

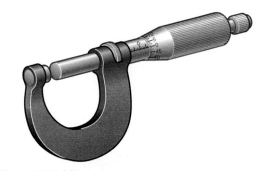

Figure 3.11 Micrometer

Figure 3.12 Electronic digital micrometer

The micrometer is used to provide measurements with great precision. The external micrometer can measure accurately to 0.01 mm. There are also electronic digital micrometers that give you the reading automatically.

QUESTION

Look at the drawing of the micrometer in figure 3.13 and state the exact reading, shown to one hundredth of a millimetre (0.01 mm).

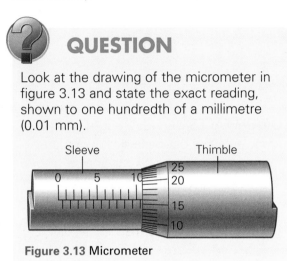

Figure 3.13 Micrometer

Surface plate marking out

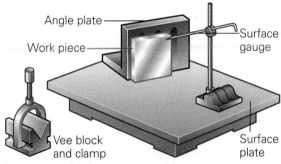

Figure 3.14 Surface plate marking out

A **surface plate** provides a flat datum surface from which very accurate measurements can be taken. The workpiece can be held against an **angle plate** or clamped in a **vee block** while being marked out using a **surface gauge**.

Gauges

Figure 3.15 Feeler gauge

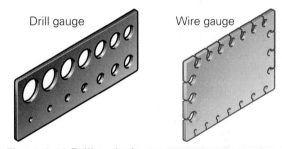

Figure 3.16 Drill and wire gauges

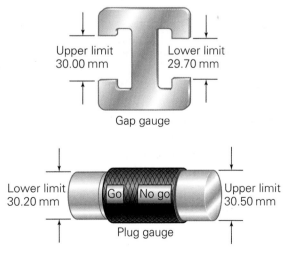

Figure 3.17 Plug and gap gauges

Feeler gauges are sets of steel blades ranging in thickness from 0.3 to 1.00 mm. The thickness is marked on each blade. The blades, or 'feelers', can be used singly or in combinations to make up a specific size. The feelers fit a gap when there is a slight pull when removing them from the clearance.

Wire gauges are used to measure the thickness of wire and, more commonly, sheet metal.

Drill gauges are used to find out the diameter of drills and round bar.

Gap gauges are used to check thicknesses.

Plug gauges are used for checking the sizes of holes.

Templates

Templates can be used to draw or cut round unusual shapes or when a shape has to be repeated for batch production. Templates can be made quickly from paper or card, but more hard-wearing materials such as thin sheet wood, metal or plastic are used in industry when the template may be used many times.

KEY TERM

DATUM FACES are sides, edges or ends of material that are perfectly flat and are used to measure or mark out from. Without a flat surface to work from, all your measurements will be inaccurate.

ACTIVITY

Complete a table similar to that shown below, listing as many different measuring, marking-out or testing tools and equipment as possible. Show the combination of materials that each could be used on and put a tick in the end column if you have used the tool or equipment.

Measuring, marking-out or testing tool or equipment	Wood	Metal	Plastic	Have I used it?
Steel rule	√	√	√	√
Try square	√	√	√	√

EXAMINER'S TIPS

Examiners often ask students to name a wasting process that could be carried out by hand or using a machine.

It is important that you know which tools or items of equipment are used. This will include the method of holding the work securely while carrying out wasting processes.

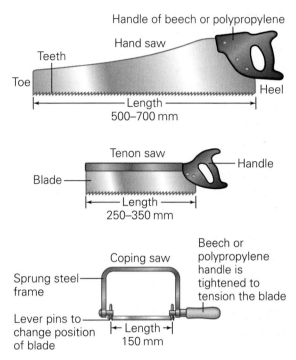

Figure 3.18 Hand saw, tenon saw and coping saw

Wasting

Wasting is concerned with the way that material is removed by cutting pieces off or cutting pieces out.

Sawing

Handsaw is the general name for saws used to saw along or across the grain of large pieces of wood. The ripsaw is used along the grain, while the cross-cut saw is used to cut across the grain.

Tenon saws are a general-purpose saw. You are likely to have used this saw more than any other as it is very good at making straight cuts in wood.

Coping saws are used to cut curves in thin wood and plastic. Care must be taken when using them because the blades can be broken quite easily. The blade should be fitted so that the teeth point backwards.

Hacksaws are used to make straight cuts in metal. The blade is held tightly in the frame, with the teeth pointing forwards.

Junior hacksaws are used in exactly the same way as the hacksaw, but on lighter or smaller-scale work. Both hacksaws can be used to cut plastic with care.

Sheet saws are a combination of a handsaw and a hacksaw, which makes them very good for cutting sheet wood, metal or plastic.

Abrafile saw 'blades' are designed to fit into a hacksaw frame. The round 'blade' can be used to cut curves in wood, metal and plastic.

Piercing saws are used for fine, intricate jewellery work, usually in metal, but they can be used to cut plastics. The blades have extremely fine teeth which can be broken easily if misused.

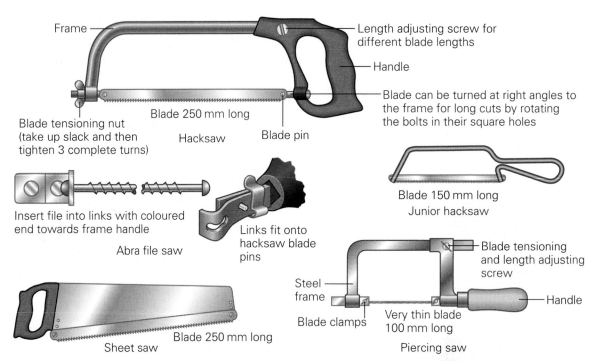

Frame

Length adjusting screw for different blade lengths

Handle

Blade can be turned at right angles to the frame for long cuts by rotating the bolts in their square holes

Blade 250 mm long

Blade tensioning nut (take up slack and then tighten 3 complete turns)

Hacksaw

Blade pin

Insert file into links with coloured end towards frame handle

Abra file saw

Links fit onto hacksaw blade pins

Blade 150 mm long
Junior hacksaw

Blade tensioning and length adjusting screw

Steel frame

Handle

Blade clamps

Very thin blade 100 mm long

Blade 250 mm long

Sheet saw

Piercing saw

Figure 3.19 Hacksaw, junior hacksaw, sheet saw, abrafile saw and piercing saw

Machine saws such as the **scroll saw** are very versatile.

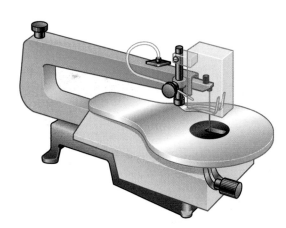

Figure 3.20 Scroll saw

Figure 3.21 Jigsaw

The **jigsaw** is extremely useful for cutting shapes from sheet material and has the advantage of being portable. Blades for both saws are interchangeable for wood, metal and plastic, and are available in fine, medium and coarse grades for different purposes.

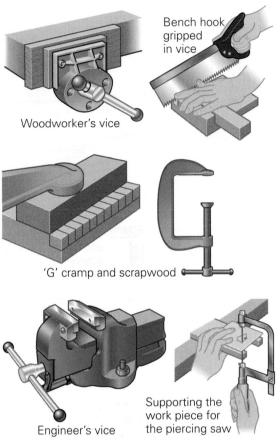

Wood that is sawn using a handsaw or a jigsaw would usually be held across a workbench because of the size of wood being sawn.

When using tenon and coping saws, the woodworker's vice would be used to secure the workpiece. A bench hook can also be used to cut small section pieces of wood. An engineer's vice is used when working with a hacksaw or an abrafile saw. Sometimes it is useful to clamp work flat onto a cutting board on a workbench. The cutting board prevents the saw blade from damaging the bench, while the scrap wood can be used as a guide for the blade and prevent bruising to the wooden workpiece. The metal cut when using the piercing saw would be supported over the edge of a workbench.

Woodworker's vice

Bench hook gripped in vice

'G' cramp and scrapwood

Engineer's vice

Supporting the work piece for the piercing saw

Figure 3.22 Methods of holding work securely

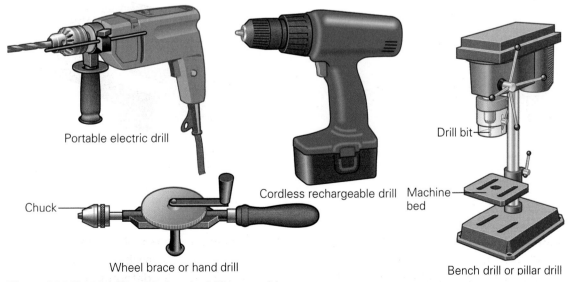

Portable electric drill

Chuck

Wheel brace or hand drill

Cordless rechargeable drill

Drill bit

Machine bed

Bench drill or pillar drill

Figure 3.23 Hand drills and electric drilling machines

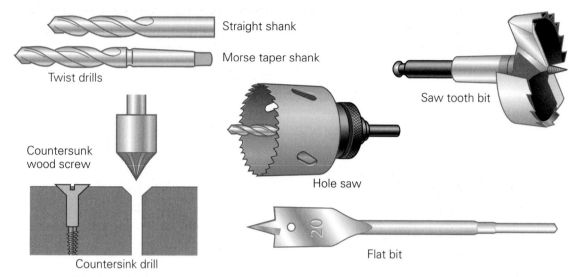

Figure 3.24 Drills and bits fitting into chucks of hand drills and electric drilling machines

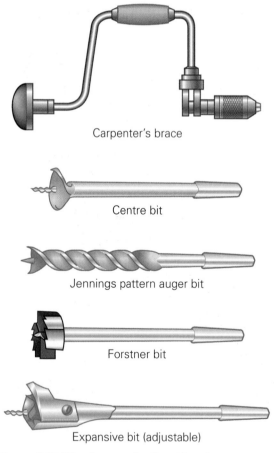

Figure 3.25 Bits that can be fitted in a brace

Drilling

There are many different types of drills and bits used when drilling holes in wood, metal and plastics. The drills and bits can be held in either a drilling machine, a portable drill, a brace or a centre lathe.

Twist drills are used for drilling holes in wood, metal and plastic. Straight shanks fit into the chuck of a drilling machine, while morse-taper shanks fit directly into the drilling machine spindles and centre lathe tailstocks.

Countersink drills provide the countersunk shape for screws.

Flat bits provide fast and accurate drilling in solid wood. The point is positioned before the drill is switched on and is left in the wood until the drill stops.

Hole saws enable you to drill holes 20–75 mm diameter. The hole saw has interchangeable cutters and removes the wood in the shape of a flat washer.

Sawtooth bits will drill out smooth-sided, flat-bottomed holes quickly and efficiently.

Centre bits are used for boring shallow holes in wood. They are unsuitable for deep holes because they have no auger (flute) to take away the waste and no parallel sides to guide it.

Jennings auger bits, or twist bits, are designed for drilling deep holes.

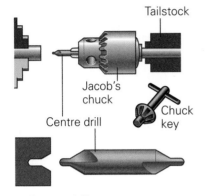

Figure 3.26 Centre drill

Forstner bits are guided by their rim rather than a centre point. They provide smooth-sided, flat-bottomed holes.

Expansive bits can be adjusted to drill shallow holes in wood 12–150 mm diameter.

A **centre drill** is used in a centre lathe to provide a 'start' when drilling into the end of a bar.

Advice when drilling/boring holes

- Make sure that the work is secure. Do not hold work with your fingers when using the drilling machine.
- If you are drilling straight through material, place scrap wood underneath to drill into.
- Make sure that the drill is tight in the

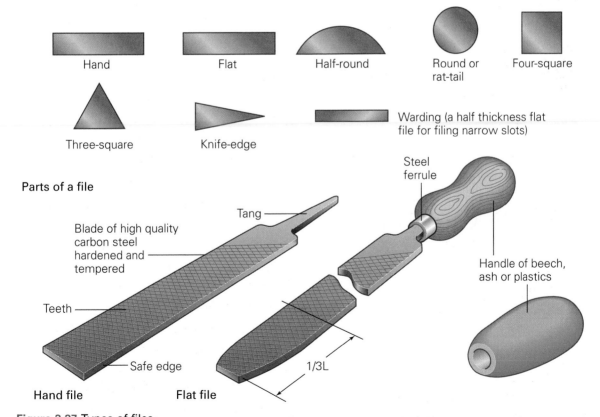

Figure 3.27 Types of files

chuck, remove the key and ensure that the safety guard is in place.

- Centre-punch metal before drilling to prevent the drill tip from 'wandering'.
- Generally, the larger the drill, the slower the speed; the smaller the drill, the faster the speed.
- When drilling large-diameter holes, drill a 'pilot' hole first.

▶ Filing

Files are made from hardened and tempered high-carbon steel. They have rows of small teeth that work like very small chisels to produce 'filings'. Files are used to shape and smooth mainly metal, plastics and wood.

Classification of files

Files are classified by length, shape and cut.

Types of cut of teeth

There are various grades of cut: rough and bastard cuts for coarse work; second cut for general use; and smooth and dead smooth for very fine work before polishing.

The shape of each file is designed to be used to produce a similar shape on the material it is cutting.

The hand file has a **safe edge** (without any teeth) that allows it to file in a 90-degree corner without removal of material on the vertical surface.

Figure 3.28 Needle file

Needle files are used for intricate work. They have dead smooth cuts and are available in a wide variety of shapes for different purposes.

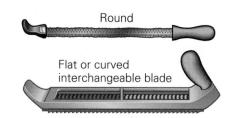

Figure 3.29 Surform tools

Surform tools have a cutting action similar to a cheese grater. They can remove wood very quickly. The most common shaped blades are flat, curved and round.

Methods of filing

Cross filing uses the full length of the file and is used to remove waste material quickly. It does not leave a smooth surface.

Draw filing is used to produce a smooth surface after cross filing. Only part of the file is used and very little material is removed.

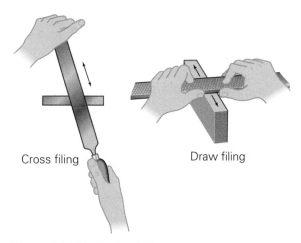

Cross filing   Draw filing

Figure 3.30 Methods of filing

▶ Chiselling

Chisels are used to cut and shape wood. You are likely to have used a chisel when cutting a joint in wood.

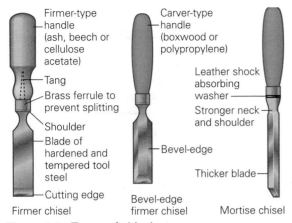

Firmer-type handle (ash, beech or cellulose acetate)

Tang

Brass ferrule to prevent splitting

Shoulder

Blade of hardened and tempered tool steel

Cutting edge

Firmer chisel

Carver-type handle (boxwood or polypropylene)

Leather shock absorbing washer

Stronger neck and shoulder

Bevel-edge

Thicker blade

Bevel-edge firmer chisel

Mortise chisel

Figure 3.31 Types of chisel

The **firmer chisel** is the general-purpose chisel that can withstand light blows from a mallet.

The **bevel-edge chisel** is different to the firmer chisel in that it has bevelled or sloping edges that allow it to be used in acute angle corners, for example, when cutting out a dovetail joint.

The **mortise chisel** is designed to be hit with a mallet. It has a thicker blade than the other chisels, which allows it to lever out waste wood without it breaking.

Methods of chiselling

Paring describes how chisels are used with hand pressure only. Safety is essential, and the most important rule is that you must keep both hands behind the cutting edge of the chisel at all times.

Horizontal paring would be used with the wood secured in a vice. It is good practice to rest the chisel on the top of the vice when paring. You would use horizontal paring to cut out a halving or housing joint.

Vertical paring from above requires considerable pressure and a G cramp is used

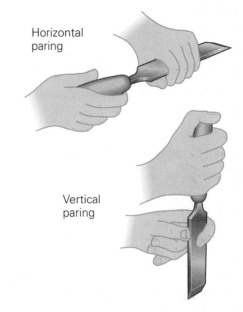

Horizontal paring

Vertical paring

Figure 3.32 Horizontal and vertical paring

to secure the wood. You may need to use a mallet to provide enough force to cut through the fibres of the wood.

Planing

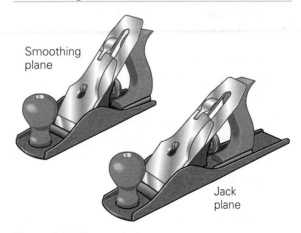

Smoothing plane

Jack plane

Figure 3.33 Types of plane

Jack planes are 350 mm long and are used for the quick removal of waste wood to make surfaces flat and to achieve the required size.

Smoothing planes are 250 mm long; they have a blade that is ground and sharpened for fine finishing and for planing end grain.

There are numerous 'special' planes that you may have seen in your workshop.

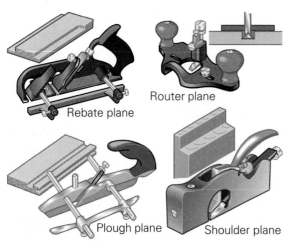

Figure 3.34 Special planes

Rebate planes cut out rebates. A stopped rebate can only be partly cut out with a plane. A small area would need to be chiselled out first to allow the plane to stop before planing right through.

Router planes are used to cut out housings across the grain of wood. They are also used to level the bottom of housings.

Plough planes are used to cut grooves and rebates.

Shoulder planes are used to clean up and level the shoulders of joints.

How a plane works

The cutting action of a plane is similar to that of a chisel held in a frame at a specific angle. Plane blades need to be ground, sharpened and set accurately for them to work effectively. If you think the plane you are

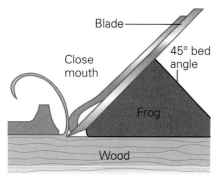

Figure 3.35 Jack plane blade

using is not cutting properly, ask your teacher to check it rather than adjusting it yourself.

Always plane along the grain; otherwise you will tear the surface of the wood. To find out which way the grain is running, look at an edge and follow the grain markings to the surface.

When planing an edge it is important to secure the wood in a vice.

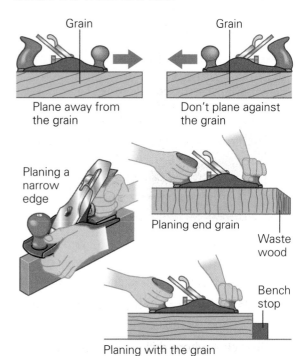

Figure 3.36 Methods of planing

When planing long thin strips of wood, use a bench stop, as the bench itself will support the strip and stop it from bending.

End grain poses problems because of the danger of splitting if the plane is taken straight across the end of the wood. One method of preventing this is to tighten a piece of scrap wood of the same thickness at one end, allowing you to plane right across. A second method is to plane to the middle of the wood, stop, and then plane to the middle from the other end. This method only works on wide boards as it can be difficult to control and stop the plane.

Centre-lathe turning

Centre lathes are used to make round components from metal and plastic. The workpiece is held securely and rotates while a single-point cutting tool cuts the material. The material can also be drilled when a drill is locked in the tailstock.

The four main parts of the centre lathe are:

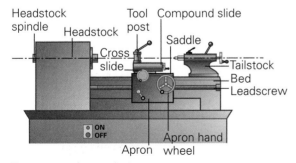

Figure 3.37 Centre lathe

- **bed** – on which the other parts are positioned
- **headstock** – containing the gearbox used to drive the workpiece
- **tailstock** – where drill chucks can be inserted and for supporting long workpieces

- **saddle** – which, as its name suggests, fits over the bed of the lathe and moves along it, carrying the cross slide and the tool post.

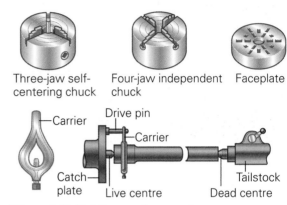

Figure 3.38 Holding work securely

The **three-jaw self-centering chuck** secures round or hexagonal materials. The three jaws come together 'automatically' to tighten the workpiece. Similar chucks are used in hand drills and drilling machines.

The **four-jaw independent chuck** is used to secure square or irregular-shaped material. Each jaw is tightened individually. Checking that the workpiece is rotating truly takes time, and therefore it is better if the turning operation can be carried out at one session rather than having to realign the material in the chuck.

The faceplate has a series of slots and holes to enable irregular-shaped work to be bolted to it.

Long pieces of work can be turned 'between centres'. The workpiece must first be faced off to make it flat, and then centre-drilled so that the 'dead' centre (the centre that does not move) and the 'live' centre (the centre that drives the workpiece) can be located and tightened.

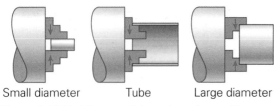

Small diameter　　Tube　　Large diameter

Figure 3.39 Holding work in a three-jaw self-centering chuck

The three-jaw chuck is the most commonly used and is very versatile. This chuck has two sets of three jaws. One set of jaws is used for small-diameter material and tube that can be secured on its inside surface. A second set of jaws enables large-diameter work to be held securely.

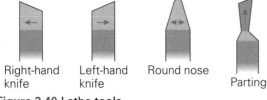

Right-hand knife　Left-hand knife　Round nose　Parting

Figure 3.40 Lathe tools

Knife tools are used to face off, cut shoulders on work or cut material off along the length of the workpiece.

There are right- and left-handed versions, depending on the direction you are working from.

Round-nosed tools can be used for left-to-right or right-to-left turning and also enable rounded or radiused corners to be cut.

Parting tools are used to make grooves in the workpiece or to cut it off.

Rake　Clearance　Correct height　　Too high Clearance lost, resulting in rubbing　　Too low Rake lost, tool will not cut

Figure 3.41 Setting lathe tools to the correct height

Lathework operations

Facing off is where the tool moves across the end of the workpiece at 90 degrees to make a flat surface.

Parallel turning is where the tool moves along the length of the workpiece to produce a round shape.

Taper turning is where the tool moves along the length of the work to produce a conical shape. Taper turning is also used to produce chamfers.

Parting off is where the tool is used to cut grooves or to cut off the workpiece. Care is needed when carrying out these operations:

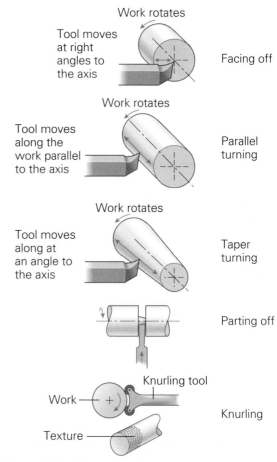

Figure 3.42 Lathe operations

Material	Cutting speed (m/min)	Cutting fluid/lubricant
Aluminium	300	None or paraffin
Brass	90	None
Mild steel	30	Soluble oil
Cast iron	20	None
Tool steel	15	Soluble oil
Nylon	200	None
Acrylic	200	None

Table 3.1 Cutting speeds and lubrication

the tool should be 'fed' slowly, withdrawn and moved along before reinserting it.

Knurling is where a tool is 'pressed' against the surface of the workpiece to produce a diamond-knurled surface. The tool has two very hard wheels pivoted in a swivelling head.

Wood turning

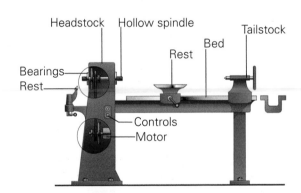

Figure 3.43 Wood-turning lathe

There are two types of turning that can be carried out on a wood-turning lathe:

- between-centres turning
- faceplate turning.

Between-centres turning

Between-centres turning is used to make products such as chair or stool legs and rolling pins.

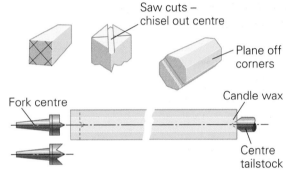

Figure 3.44 Between-centres turning

A fork centre is pushed into the spindle in the headstock; this drives the workpiece as it is connected directly to the motor. In the tailstock, a dead centre is pushed in; this simply supports the workpiece while it rotates. The workpiece needs to be prepared before it can be mounted on the lathe. A saw cut is made in one end of the wood so that the fork centre can fit tightly to drive the wood. The edges of the wood are planed off to make turning easier to start and to prevent splitting.

Faceplate turning

Faceplate turning is used to make products such as bowls.

The workpiece should have the corners removed to help the start of turning. It is then

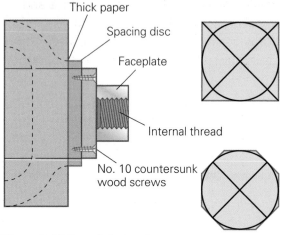

Figure 3.45 Faceplate turning

glued to a similar size and shape of scrap wood with thick paper sandwiched in between. This is then screwed onto a faceplate. The faceplate with the wood attached can then be screwed onto the headstock spindle, ready to turn.

Procedures

- The tool rest must be as close to the workpiece as possible. Always spin the work by hand to make sure that it does not 'catch' the tool rest.

- Lathe speeds are generally as follows: the larger the diameter of wood to be turned, the slower the speed; the smaller the diameter, the faster the speed.

- Scrapers are the safest type of turning tool to use. Gouges require more care and skill.

- Use outside calipers to test the diameter required. On complicated shapes it is best to use a template.

▶ Milling

Milling machines are used to cut slots and grooves and for machining large surfaces of metal or plastic to make them flat.

The workpiece is fixed to a table that can move backwards and forwards while the material is cut. The table can also be raised and lowered. A variety of different cutters can be used, depending on the type of job. Coolant is applied to the cutters constantly to reduce the heat generated and wear.

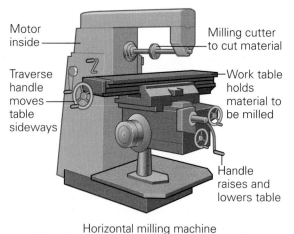

Horizontal milling machine

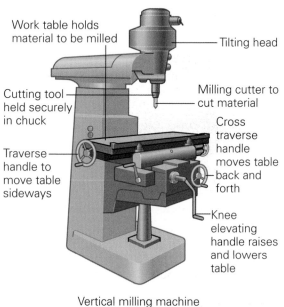

Vertical milling machine

Figure 3.46 Milling machines

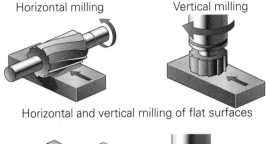

Horizontal milling   Vertical milling

Horizontal and vertical milling of flat surfaces

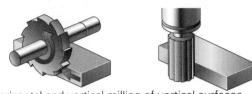

Horizontal and vertical milling of vertical surfaces – the horizontal machine is using a side and face cutter which cuts on its side and on its diameter

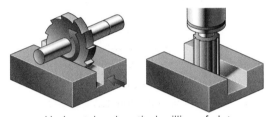

Horizontal and vertical milling of slots

Figure 3.47 Milling operations

Routing

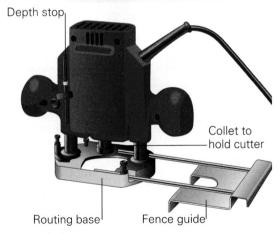

Depth stop

Collet to hold cutter

Routing base   Fence guide

Figure 3.48 Power router

The power router is an extremely useful tool when cutting joints and shapes in wood that would traditionally be cut using planes and chisels. They can be dangerous to use and therefore must not be used unless you have been shown by your teacher and supervised directly.

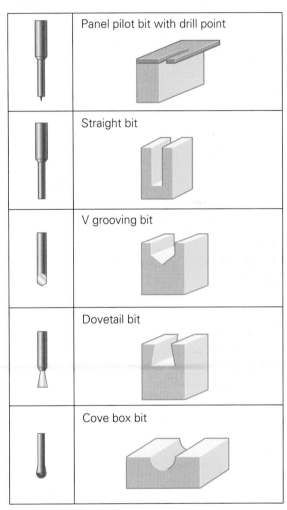

	Panel pilot bit with drill point
	Straight bit
	V grooving bit
	Dovetail bit
	Cove box bit

Figure 3.49 Types of routing bits/cutters

Routing operation

Set the tool base on the workpiece to be cut without the bit making any contact. Then turn the machine on and wait until the bit is at full speed. Lower the machine body and move the tool forwards over the workpiece surface,

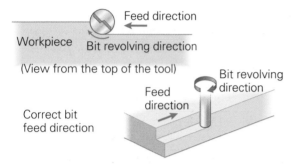

Figure 3.50 Correct bit-feed direction

keeping the routing base flush and advancing smoothly until the cutting is complete.

When doing edge cutting, the workpiece surface should be on the left side of the bit in the feed direction (see figure 3.50).

Moving the tool forward too fast may cause a poor quality of cut or damage to the bit or motor. Moving the tool forward too slowly may burn and affect the cut. The proper feed rate will depend on the bit size, the kind of workpiece and the depth of cut. Before beginning the cut on the actual workpiece, it is advisable to make a sample cut on a piece of scrap wood. This will show exactly how the cut will look.

Laser cutting

KEY POINT

- Laser stands for 'light amplification by stimulated emission of radiation' and lasers are being used more and more for a wide range of processes, including the cutting of virtually any material.

Laser cutting is a thermal process in which a focused laser beam is used to burn or melt material in a tiny localised area or 'dot'. A continuous cut in the material is produced by moving the laser beam (and, in some cases, the workpiece) under **computer control**. The main advantages of laser cutting are that it gives a clean cut and is also very accurate. Laser-cutting machines for use in schools and colleges are normally quite low-powered for use on woods, plastics and some thin sheet metals. When used for cutting metals and plastics, the low heat input of the laser means that the material is less likely to distort than when using other processes.

Figure 3.51 A school-size laser cutter

Figure 3.52 Example of work done by laser cutter

For industrial use, much larger and higher-powered machines are widely used and are particularly useful for cutting complex shapes out of sheet metal. Because the laser 'cut' is very narrow, the cutting speed is high and, in addition to this, parts can be positioned close together, meaning that less waste is produced.

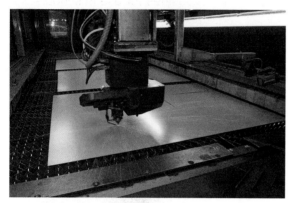

Figure 3.53 An industrial laser cutter

Screw cutting

Threading is the term to describe screw threads cut on the outside of round rod. This is done by means of a circular split die held in a diestock.

Tapping is the term used to describe screw threads cut on the inside of a hole. This is done by means of taps held in a tap wrench.

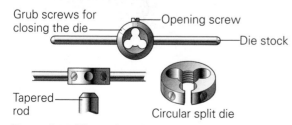

Figure 3.54 Diestock and die

Threading

1. When starting, always try to press down firmly and squarely to avoid a 'drunken' thread.

2. Use the appropriate lubricant.

3. Chamfer the end of the rod to make it easier to start cutting the thread.

4. Fit the circular split die into the diestock with the size information showing.

5. Tighten the middle screw to open the die for the first cut.

6. Tighten the two outer screws for the next cut if you find that the thread is too tight a fit when screwed into the inside thread.

7. When applying pressure to cut into the material, you will need to turn or 'ease back' the die to break off the swarf and remove the cuttings.

Tapping

This is exactly the same process except that three taps may need to be used.

Figure 3.55 Tap wrench and taps

The taper tap is used to make it easier when starting and can be used on its own in thin material.

The second tap is used to make threads started by the taper tap deeper.

The plug tap is used to cut full threads in 'blind' holes and in thicker material.

Taps are made from high-speed steel (HSS). They are very brittle and you will need to be very careful when using them.

Remember that the tapping drill size will be slightly smaller than the size of screw thread to cut.

Table 3.2 shows some tapping drill sizes.

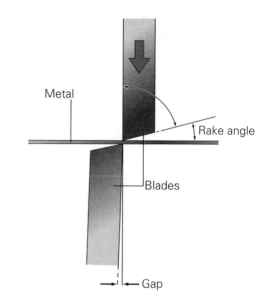

Figure 3.56 Shearing action

Screw thread size	Tapping drill size
M2	1.6
M3	2.5
M4	3.3
M5	4.2
M6	5.0
M8	6.8
M10	8.5
M12	10.2

Table 3.2 Tapping drill sizes

Shearing

Shearing is the action of tinsnips or bench shears when cutting sheet metal. It is similar to that of a pair of scissors, with one blade passing another.

Tinsnips and **bench shears** will cut through aluminium, copper and even thin mild steel sheet.

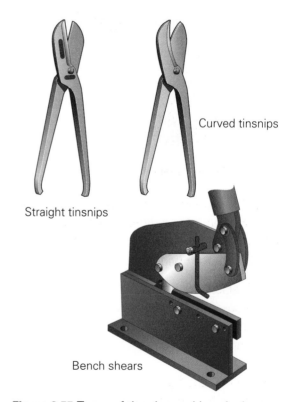

Figure 3.57 Types of tinsnips and bench shears

When using tinsnips, make sure that the sheet metal is pushed right back between the two blades. If you only use the end of the blades there is a possibility that you will twist the metal. Often one handle is secured in an engineer's vice and the sheet metal is fed between the blades, with pressure placed on the movable handle.

Bench shears can be used to cut thin rod and strip as well as sheet metal. The long handle of the bench shears provides a lot more leverage than tinsnips.

Cold chisels can shear sheet metal when it is secured in a vice.

Cutting sheet metal in the vice

Figure 3.58 Cutting sheet metal in a vice

Cold chisels are made from high-carbon steel, have a cutting edge ground to a 60-degree angle, are at least 100 mm long and vary from 6 to 25 mm wide.

The chisel is held at 30 degrees to the workpiece, with one side of it resting on the vice, while a cut is made on the waste side of the line.

Blanking and piercing

Blanking is the operation of cutting out a piece of metal of the required shape by using a punch and a die. In this case, it is the removed piece of metal that is important and not the hole produced.

Piercing is the operation of producing a hole of any shape in a sheet of metal using a punch and a die. The material removed is unimportant and is treated as scrap. 'Punching' is similar to piercing, but refers to the production of a circular hole.

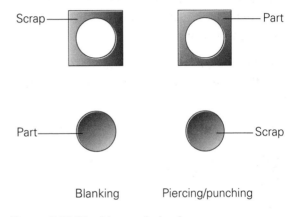

Blanking   Piercing/punching

Figure 3.59 Blanking and piercing

KEY POINT

Forming processes are those that allow shapes to be produced with the minimum amount of wastage of material. They are particularly important when making large numbers of items because great savings in material are made, and also because the cost of removing material to make the shape required is reduced and in some cases eliminated completely.

KEY TERMS

WASTING is concerned with the way that material is removed by cutting pieces off or cutting pieces out.

FACING OFF is the tool moving across the end of the workpiece at 90 degrees to make a flat surface.

PARALLEL TURNING is where the tool moves along the length of the workpiece to produce a round shape.

TAPER TURNING is where the tool moves along the length of the work to produce a conical shape. Taper turning is also used to produce chamfers.

PARTING OFF is where the tool is used to make grooves or to cut off the workpiece.

KNURLING is where a tool is 'pressed' against the surface of the workpiece to produce a diamond-knurled surface. The tool has two very hard wheels pivoted in a swivelling head.

BETWEEN-CENTRES TURNING is used to make products such as chair or stool legs and rolling pins.

FACEPLATE TURNING is used to make products such as bowls.

THREADING is the term used to describe screw threads cut on the outside of round rod.

TAPPING is the term used to describe screw threads cut on the inside of tube.

SHEARING is the action of tinsnips or bench shears when cutting sheet metal. It is similar to that of a pair of scissors, with one blade passing another.

BLANKING is the operation of cutting out a piece of metal of the required shape by using a punch and a die. In this case, it is the removed piece of metal that is important and not the hole produced.

PIERCING is the operation of producing a hole of any shape in a sheet of metal using a punch and a die. The material removed is unimportant and is treated as scrap.

SAFE EDGE The hand file has a safe edge (without any teeth) that allows it to file in a 90-degree corner without removal of material on the vertical surface.

CROSS FILING uses the full length of the file and is used to remove waste material quickly. It does not leave a smooth surface.

DRAW FILING is used to produce a smooth surface after cross filing. Only part of the file is used and very little material is removed.

Forming Processes

There are many processes that can be used to form resistant materials, some of which can easily be done in the school workshop. Although most forming processes are designed to be used for a particular material, some of the simpler processes can be used on a range of different materials. New processes are continually being developed, but all forming processes can be divided into two groups. The largest group is 'deforming' processes, which are those that form the material while it is in the solid state. A smaller number of processes are classed as 'reforming' processes, because the material has to be changed into a liquid before being formed into the required shape and returned to solid.

KEY TERMS

FORMING PROCESSES used to make shaped parts without wasting material or time by machining

DEFORMING processes, such as bending, that shape the material while it is in the sold state

REFORMING processes involving changing the state of the material.

▶ Deforming processes

Wood

KEY POINT

- The number of processes that can be used to deform wood is very limited because of the nature of the material. Wood will only bend by a very small amount before it breaks and this makes forming very difficult. As wood cuts more easily than other resistant materials, it is common for wood products to be made by machining (a wasting process).

Bending

A very basic method of **bending** wood into curves is called **kerfing**, which involves putting a series of evenly spaced saw cuts in the timber to allow it to be bent. It is only

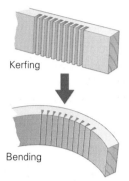

Figure 3.60 Kerfing wood

really suitable if just one side of the curve is to be visible, such as for the curved side of a guitar body. As the wood is bent into a curve, the edges of the saw cuts close up to each other and a smooth curve is produced on the outside of the bend.

One method of deforming wood that has been used for many years is **steam bending**. This involves placing the wood in a sealed chest which is kept filled with steam at 100 °C so that the wood absorbs the hot moisture and becomes softer and easy to bend. The amount of time needed to soften the wood sufficiently for bending depends on the timber being used, but most timbers are steamed for one hour for every 25 mm of thickness before they are taken out for bending.

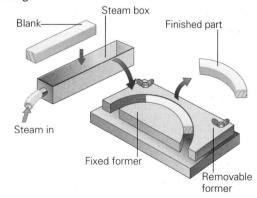

Figure 3.61 Steam bending timber

The steamed wood is bent into the required shape around a special **former** and clamped firmly in place so that it keeps its shape while it dries out. The shaped wood needs to dry out thoroughly before it is unclamped, otherwise it is likely to twist as further drying takes place.

Laminating

The other, and more commonly used, method of producing **'bent wood'** shapes is laminating, in which the shape required is built up from thin layers of wood called **veneers**. In this way, any thickness can be produced and tighter bends can be achieved than by steaming solid timber. The layers of veneer are glued together, using one of the many strong modern adhesives available, and then clamped around a former until the adhesive is set. The method used to clamp the laminated shape depends on the size and complexity of the shape being produced, and the number required. Typical clamping arrangements include specially shaped blocks, standard G or sash cramps, flexible steel bands and vacuum bags. Care must be taken to ensure that the laminated shape does not become glued to the former, and it is normal to use wax on the formers to stop

the adhesive sticking to them, or to place thin rubber strips between the shape and the formers.

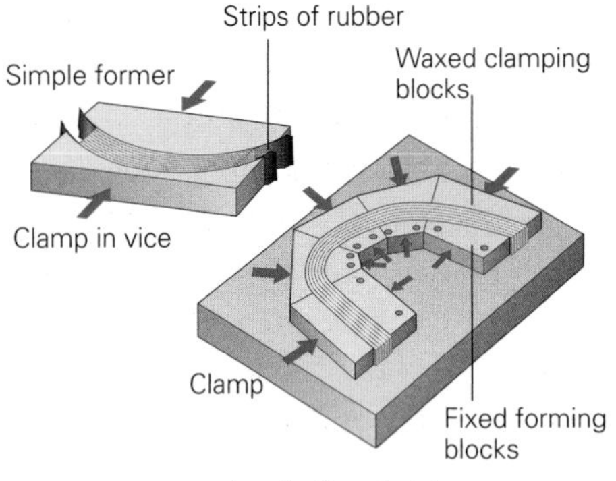

The construction of the shaped form looks quite similar to plywood, but the grain of each layer of veneer runs in the same direction, following the shape of the curve, whereas with plywood the grains of alternate layers run at 90 degrees to each other.

KEY TERMS

KERFING – Making saw cuts so that wood can bend.
STEAM BENDING – Softening the fibres of wood with steam to allow it to bend.
FORMER – A block made to hold material in the shape required.
LAMINATING – Building up a shape in thin layers.

EXAMINER'S TIPS

If an examination question asks you to use **sketches and notes** in your answer, always make sure that you use **both**. The notes (annotation) help you to explain more clearly what it is that your sketch shows.

ACTIVITY

The back legs of the mahogany chair in figure 3.63 are curved to make the chair more stable and to improve the appearance of the chair. Use sketches and notes to explain how the legs could be shaped if:

Strips of rubber / Simple former / Waxed clamping blocks / Clamp in vice / Clamp / Fixed forming blocks
Laminating chair legs

Figure 3.62 Forming laminated wooden shapes

(a) they were made from solid mahogany

(b) they were made from pine and covered with a mahogany veneer.

In each case, the legs must be made by forming and not by cutting the shape out of a larger piece of wood.

Figure 3.63 Mahogany chair

Metal

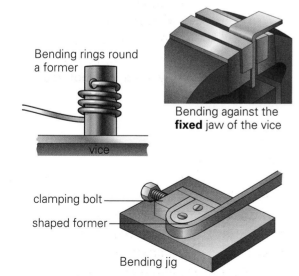

Bending rings round a former

vice

Bending against the **fixed** jaw of the vice

clamping bolt

shaped former

Bending jig

Figure 3.64 Examples of metal bending

KEY POINT

- Unlike wood, most metals are **malleable** or can be made more malleable by using heat. This means that they can be deformed without cracking, and shaped metal parts can be produced by a number of processes.

Bending

Simple bends can be produced by holding the metal in a bench vice and hammering it into shape. Depending on the metal and its thickness, this can be done either hot or cold, and thinner metal sections can often be bent by hand. When bending non-ferrous metals such as copper, brass and aluminium, the metal is often annealed before bending, to make it more malleable.

If an accurate bend or a particular shape is required, this is done using a specially made former. When a number of items need to be bent to the same shape, a bending jig should be made to ensure that they are all accurately made.

Where very large numbers of parts are needed, special-purpose machines are often built to make them. All the curved parts on the **stainless steel** bench shown in figure 3.65 are made by forcing the metal strip round formers, using **hydraulic** pressure to produce the high force required to bend it. The machine is only used for the parts for this bench, but it can be used to make thousands of identical parts.

Figure 3.65 Stainless steel bench

KEY POINT

- Non-ferrous metals, such as copper, brass and aluminium, can be formed into shape using **beaten** sheet-metal working methods, to produce items such as bowls, vases and jugs. Gold and silver are particularly suitable for this type of forming and were extensively used for many years, but they are very expensive to use, and **base** metals are now often plated to give the appearance of these **precious** metals.

The most commonly used beaten metalwork processes are hollowing, sinking and raising, although some shapes in copper and brass are formed by folding or rolling flat sheet metal and then silver-soldering the edges to produce a **seam**. This is often used to produce cylinders, but it is also the best way to form straight-sided items.

Hollowing is used to produce shallow dishes and bowls and involves hammering the soft metal into a leather sandbag or a hollowed-out wooden block. This is done using an egg-shaped mallet called a **bossing** mallet that is normally made out of boxwood. A round disc of metal is cut from a sheet and then annealed to soften it. After cleaning the metal, concentric circles are drawn on the disc and the hollowing is started at the outside edge, working in, one circle at a time, to the centre.

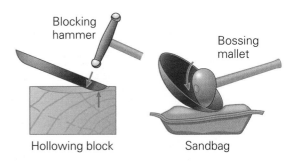

Figure 3.66 Hollowing

Sinking is quite similar to hollowing and is also used to produce shallow dishes, but with a flat rim round the top. It is carried out on a wooden block, specially shaped to give the required depth of the finished dish. Two pegs are fitted in the top of the sinking block to make sure the rim is the same width all the way round the dish. The annealed disc of metal is held against the pegs on the sinking block and hammered into the shaped part of the block using a round-faced metal **blocking** hammer or a boxwood mallet. The sinking is done gradually, working round the dish until the required depth is reached, and the rim is made flat after each round of sinking. Sinking is quite a slow process, and the metal usually needs to be annealed and cleaned several times during the forming of the dish.

Raising is carried out on shaped metal stakes. Although shallow bowls can be raised over round stakes, it is easier to make them

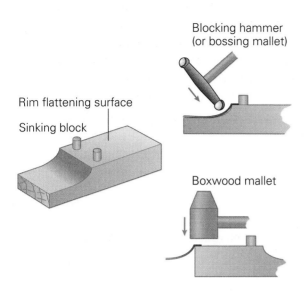

Figure 3.67 Sinking

by hollowing, and raising is normally used to form deeper items such as vases and jugs. The shape is usually started off by hollowing, but then continued using metal raising hammers on a raising stake. The shape required is made gradually deeper and narrower, working round the diameter at each stage.

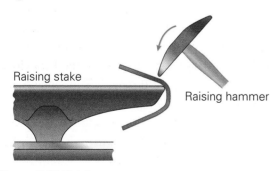

Figure 3.68 Raising

Whichever process is used to form the shaped item, it will need to be finished off by **planishing** to remove any irregularities in the shape and give a smooth, even surface. Planishing involves lightly hammering the metal against specially shaped and highly polished metal stakes, using polished planishing hammers. Each hammer blow needs to be of equal 'weight', and they should all slightly overlap each other. This leaves small **facets** on the surface of the metal which can be polished out or left as a decorative finish.

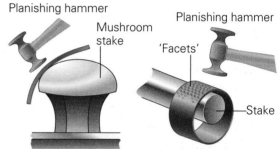

Figure 3.69 Planishing

These metal-beating processes are used for the one-off manufacture of handmade items and prototype models, as they are time-consuming and require considerable practice and skill to carry out successfully. Where large-scale production of such items is needed, this is done using presswork operations to form the required shapes; some design changes may be necessary to enable the parts to be made by quantity production methods.

KEY TERMS

HOLLOWING – Hammering softened metal into a sandbag or a hollowed-out wooden block.

SINKING – Hammering into a specially shaped wooden block to form a bowl with a flat rim.

RAISING – Making deeper items on polished metal stakes.

PLANISHING – Smoothing out surface imperfections with polished hammers and stakes.

Sheet metalwork

KEY POINT

- Sheet metalwork is used to produce hollow items such as air extraction ducts, boxes and trays from thin sheet metal, often only 1 mm thick. Many metals are suitable for use, but galvanised steel, aluminium and tinplate are the most common.

Before cutting the sheet metal to shape, a cardboard mock-up is made to check the shape, size and position of joining flaps. This is then used as the **net** (development) to mark out the required shape on the metal sheet, and cutting is done using hand shears (**tinsnips**), a bench shear or a power guillotine for larger parts.

Straight-sided objects can be folded in the vice or over wooden formers, and cylinders are produced in **bending rolls**. The metal should be protected by soft jaws if clamped in an engineer's vice, and any hammering must be done with a rawhide or nylon mallet to avoid leaving marks in the metal. Because the cut edges of the sheet metal are very sharp, a **safe edge** is normally produced by folding back a narrow flap of the material. This also stiffens the edge and helps the object to keep its shape.

When the metal has been cut to shape and folded or rolled, the joints are made by riveting, soldering or, in some cases, welding.

Figure 3.70 Bending rolls

KEY TERMS

BEATEN METALWORK – Making shaped decorative items from non-ferrous metals.

SHEET METALWORK – Making hollow objects by folding, rolling and joining thin sheet metal.

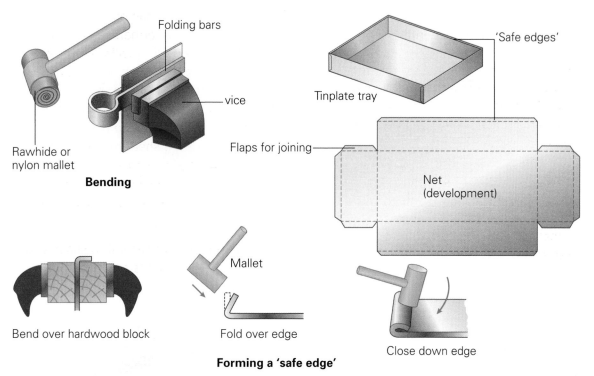

Figure 3.71 Sheet metal working

On an industrial scale, items such as galvanised steel ducting are made on specially made semi-automatic machines. The metal is cut, shaped and joined on a flow-line basis, with much use being made of robots to carry out handling and joining processes.

Figure 3.72 Galvanised steel pipework

Forging

KEY POINT

- Forging is generally considered as the process of forming metal while it is hot, although in modern industry some items can now be 'cold-forged' using very high-pressure hydraulics to 'squeeze' the metal into shape.

Hot-forging is one of the oldest methods of forming metals, and it is still used to produce shaped parts. It is particularly useful where strength is important, and steel is the metal most commonly used for forged parts. When forging, the grain of the metal is made to follow the shape of the item being produced and becomes more dense. This makes the item much stronger than cutting it from a solid block, as the grain is not interrupted and weakened.

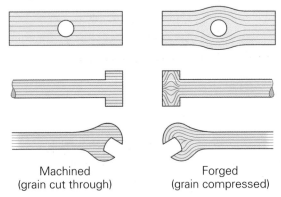

Machined
(grain cut through)

Forged
(grain compressed)

Figure 3.73 Grain flow in forged items

There are many different techniques used to forge metal, some of which are mainly to produce decorative effects such as twists and scrolls. All the techniques require skilful use of the hammer and other blacksmith's tools in the workshop, and some have been modified for use in industry for large-scale production.

A wide range of special tools are used for particular forgework processes, but the three vital pieces of equipment for general work are the **forge**, the **anvil** and the **hammer**.

A blacksmith's forge traditionally burned coke to provide the heat, but modern **ceramic chip** forges are gas-fired. The metal to be heated is pushed into the bed of ceramic chips to prevent the air oxidising the hot metal.

The anvil is the most important piece of equipment of all and is used for almost all forgework operations.

The anvil is made from mild steel and has a hardened steel **face** for hammering the hot metal on. The square **hardie hole** at the back

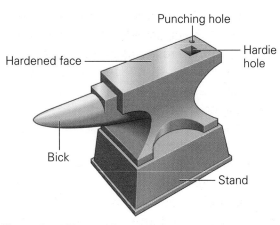

Figure 3.74 The anvil

of the face is to hold the specially shaped tools used for certain operations, and the smaller round hole is for **punching** holes in hot metal. The shape of the **bick** allows curves to be formed round it, and the whole anvil is usually mounted on a stand or a large block of wood to bring it up to a comfortable working height.

Forgework operations

Upsetting (sometimes called 'jumping up') is used to increase the thickness of a bar at a particular point. The area to be 'upset' is heated to white-hot while keeping the rest of the bar cold. The bar is then hammered on the anvil or in a vice to spread the heated metal and increase the thickness. The finished bar with its upset section is then slightly shorter than the original.

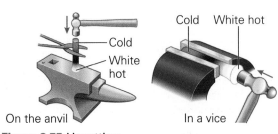

Figure 3.75 Upsetting

Upsetting is widely used in industry to form the heads of rivets, screws and bolts, when it is commonly referred to as **heading**. The process is highly automated to mass-produce the items and may be done either hot or cold, depending on the size and the metal used. Only the larger sizes are now made by 'hot' heading, as cold heading is quicker and gives a better finish. The material is fed to the automatic machine from a coil, cut to length and then transferred to a die. A specially shaped punch then forms the head on the end of the bar, and the finished item is ejected from the die to go on for threading if needed.

Scrolling and twisting operations are used to produce decorative features like those used in traditional wrought ironwork, although mild steel is now commonly used for this type of work. After heating the steel to bright red, the steel strip is thinned and bent over on the anvil before forming the scroll, which may be done on **cranking horns** or a special **scrolling iron**. A scroll may need to be reheated several times during the bending, but a twist should be completed in one operation from bright-red heat, turning the bar steadily with the **twisting wrench**.

KEY TERMS

FORGING – Hammering or squeezing metal into shape, usually when hot.
ANVIL – The main piece of equipment for hand-forging metal.
UPSETTING – Increasing the thickness of part of a hot metal bar.
CRANKING HORNS – Simple tool for bending strip metal into curves.

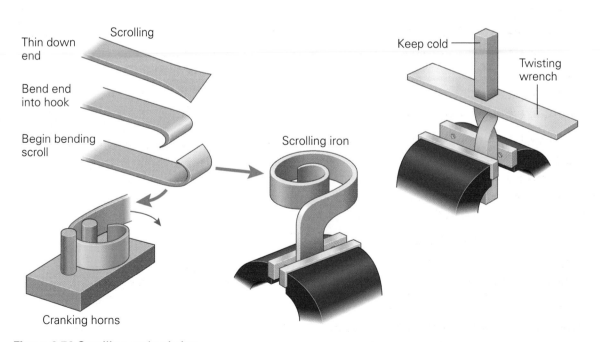

Figure 3.76 Scrolling and twisting

Plastics

KEY POINT

- **Thermoplastics** are easy to form because they can be softened by heat; there are several forming processes that can be carried out in the school workshop using quite basic equipment. Because **thermosetting** plastics cannot be softened by heat, they are normally moulded directly into the shape required and cannot then be deformed. All the processes used to **deform** thermoplastics involve heating the plastic to make it softer, and it is very important that care is taken when using these processes.

Line-bending

This is the process used to produce simple bends in plastic sheet. It is particularly useful for forming **acrylic** sheet, which can be softened by heating it to about 160 °C. The acrylic is heated along the line where the bend is to be made, and this is best done with a **strip heater**. The one shown in figure 3.77 has a long electric element that is adjustable for height. The further away from the element the plastic is, the wider the softened strip will be, and then a more gradual bend can be produced. If the plastic is positioned too close to the heating element it can overheat and burn, causing 'blistering', which ruins the surface of the plastic. To

prevent this overheating, the plastic sheet should be turned over frequently so that it is heated evenly from both sides.

When the plastic is soft enough to be flexible it will start to bend under its own weight, and it can then be removed using leather gloves and bent into shape. This is usually done using a specially shaped **former** or a **bending**

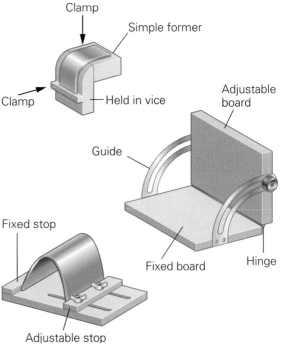

Figure 3.77 An electric strip heater

Figure 3.78 Line-bending

jig to make sure the bend is made accurately. These need to have very smooth surfaces, otherwise any grain marks or defects could become 'imprinted' in the soft plastic. It is important that the plastic is held against the former or jig until it has cooled down and becomes hard again, so that it 'sets' in the correct position.

If larger curves and bends are required, a variation on the line-bending process can be used. This is called **drape-forming**. The plastic sheet is usually heated in a temperature-controlled oven because of the width of the strip needing to be heated. The softened plastic is then 'draped' over a former, pulled tightly onto it using a length of cloth, and held there until the plastic has cooled, either by hand or using clamps.

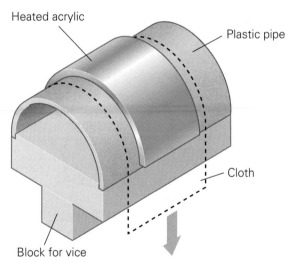

Figure 3.79 Drape-forming

Press-moulding

This process is used to produce more complex shapes, such as dishes and trays, where curves in more than one direction need to be formed. It can be used on thin acrylic sheet, and also on other thin-sheet

plastic materials such as ABS (acrylonitrile-butadiene-styrene) and HIPS (high-impact polystyrene).

Press moulding involves the use of two-part formers, consisting of a **plug** to produce the shape required, and a **yoke** to press the soft plastic over the plug. The plug should have angled sides and smooth, rounded corners so that the finished moulding is easy to remove from it. The hole in the yoke needs to be bigger than the size of the plug to allow for the thickness of the plastic sheet between them, leaving a gap of about one and a half times the thickness of the plastic. The two-part former includes **guide pegs** to make sure the plug and yoke are aligned properly as the yoke is put in place.

The plastic sheet to be moulded needs to be heated in an oven so that the whole of it is soft and flexible. It is then positioned on the plug and pushed down over it with the yoke. The two parts of the former are then clamped together to hold the plastic against the plug until it has cooled down. When the shape has 'set' it can be removed from the formers and the excess plastic cut away from the finished moulding.

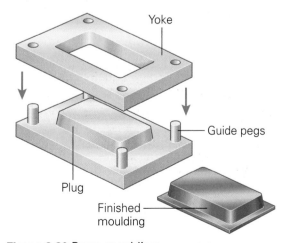

Figure 3.80 Press-moulding

Vacuum-forming

Vacuum-forming is quite similar to press-moulding in many ways, but it can be used to produce deeper and more complex shapes. The process works by creating a vacuum underneath a softened **thermoplastic** sheet, allowing atmospheric pressure to push the plastic against the mould (plug). Vacuum-forming is widely used in manufacturing, with some of the best examples being items for packaging, where very thin, clear plastic can be formed into the shape of an object to protect it and allow it to be displayed. Many of the common thermoplastics can be used, but the two you are most likely to use in project work are ABS and HIPS.

Figure 3.81 Examples of vacuum-formings

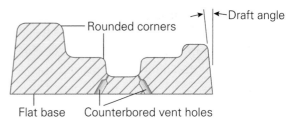

Figure 3.82 Vacuum-forming mould

material and have a smooth surface, without any marks or defects that would show up on the vacuum-forming. If a vacuum-forming is to have a number of different depths or small recesses, it is often necessary to put **vent holes** in the mould. This is to ensure that all the air can be removed quickly, as any air trapped above the mould would prevent the softened plastic forming to the exact shape required.

Figure 3.83 Vacuum-forming machine

The design of the **mould** for a vacuum forming is very important, because as well as producing the shape required it must also allow it to be easily removed from the mould after forming. The sides of the mould need to be slightly tapered to give a **draft angle**, and any corners should be **radiused** (rounded off). The rounding-off of corners is particularly important as it also reduces the risk of splitting the thin plastic as it is formed. The mould should be made from a heat-resistant

The vacuum-forming process is quite straightforward and often more than one item can be made at a time, depending on the size of the items and the size of the machine. The mould to be used is placed on the **platen** in the bottom of the machine and then a sheet of thermoplastic is clamped firmly in place to give an **airtight seal**. The heating element is then moved into position above the plastic

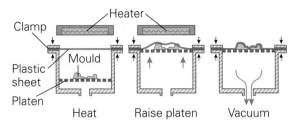

Figure 3.84 The vacuum-forming process

sheet and switched on. When the plastic is flexible enough, the platen is raised to bring the mould into place and the vacuum is switched on. The softened plastic is forced onto the mould by atmospheric pressure, and when the shape is fully formed the heat is turned off, but the vacuum is left on to allow the shape to 'set'. The 'blow' facility on the vacuum-forming machine can be used to help break the seal between the mould and the plastic after forming.

Blow-moulding

Like vacuum-forming, blow-moulding uses air pressure to form softened thermoplastic sheet material, but in this case the air is compressed and blown directly against the plastic. The simplest form of blow-moulding is called **free-blowing**. This is used to produce regular, dome-shaped objects, and the shape of the dome can be **restricted** to give a flat base for a bowl if required. The diameter of the dome or bowl produced is governed by the diameter of the hole in the **clamping ring** that holds the thermoplastic sheet in place for blowing. For free-blowing to be successful, the temperature of the plastic and the air pressure applied need to be carefully controlled, and it can be difficult to ensure that exactly the same size and shape are produced each time.

When larger numbers of items or more complex shapes are needed, the softened plastic is blown into a specially shaped **mould**. As with vacuum-forming, the design of the mould is important and must include tapered sides and rounded corners to allow the finished moulding to be removed easily from the mould.

The most common application of blow-moulding is in the manufacture of plastic bottles and other containers. In this application the blow-moulding is carried out as part of a fully automated process that includes **extrusion** (this is covered in more detail later, page 133).

Blow-moulding and vacuum-forming are both processes that can readily be adapted to suit particular products, and in some cases they can also be combined. Large items made from fairly thick plastic sheet, such as acrylic baths, can be made by vacuum-forming the shape in the normal way, but also using compressed air to force the plastic into the deep mould during forming.

KEY TERMS

MOULD – Made to the shape required to be used many times.
LINE-BENDING – Bending plastic after softening a narrow strip.
PRESS-MOULDING – Forming a hollow shape from a softened plastic sheet.
VACUUM-FORMING – Producing thin hollow items over a shaped mould.
BLOW-MOULDING – Using air pressure to blow softened plastic into shape.

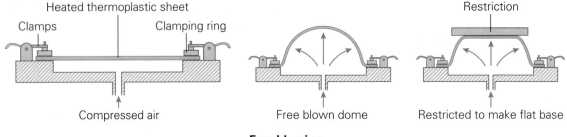

Free blowing

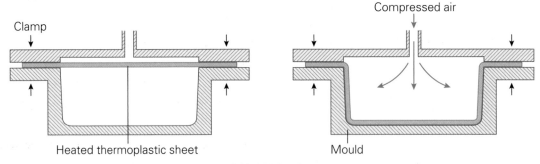

Mould blowing

Figure 3.85 Blow-moulding

ACTIVITY

The small storage box shown in figure 3.86 has been made by vacuum-forming ABS plastic. The box has sloping sides so that empty boxes can be stacked together for storage.

A lid is needed to fit into the top of the box to allow boxes to be stacked on top of each other when they are being used.

Figure 3.86 Plastic storage box

Design and make a mould for producing the box and the lid together on one sheet of plastic.

Draw a simple labelled sketch of the mould, showing the sizes for each part.

The size of the box can be made to suit the vacuum-forming machine you have in your school workshop. When you have vacuum-formed the box and lid, check that the two parts fit together properly and comment on any problems you might find.

❱ Fabricating

Fabricating is to do with the way materials are joined together.

EXAMINER'S TIPS

Examiners often ask questions about 'temporary' and 'permanent' methods of joining materials. Make sure you know the difference between these methods.

Temporary methods of fabrication

Temporary means that the method of joining can be taken apart. These include the use of screws, nuts and bolts and KD fittings, which are known as pre-manufactured standard components. These are dealt with in chapter 2.

Permanent methods of fabrication

Permanent means that once the materials have been joined they will remain joined for ever. These include the use of adhesives with wood, metal and plastics, riveting metal and heat processes used to join metal.

Adhesives

PVA adhesive such as Evostik Resin 'W'.

- Good general woodworking adhesive.
- Ready-mixed for ease of use.
- Water-resistant varieties available.
- Takes two to four hours to set and requires pressure through clamping.
- Few health and safety problems.

Contact adhesive such as Alpha/Dunlop Thixofix® or Evostik Time Bond.

- Used to glue plastic laminate to manufactured boards (suitable for large areas).

- Apply evenly to both surfaces to be glued.
- Leave until 'touch-dry' (10–15 minutes).
- Position two surfaces accurately before applying final pressure to the two surfaces in contact.
- Precaution: because most of these adhesives set when the surfaces come into contact with each other, accurate positioning is essential.

Synthetic resin adhesive such as Cascamite.

- Excellent woodworking adhesive, especially designed for boat building or any work in contact with water.
- White glue powder mixed with water to a creamy consistency.
- When mixed must be used within 30 minutes; wasteful if not used up.
- Apply to joints and cramp together under pressure and allow six hours to set.

Epoxy resin adhesive such as Araldite™.

- Used to glue together a variety of materials: wood, metal, some plastics, ceramics, glass.
- Two parts in two tubes: resin (glue) and hardener (catalyst).
- Two parts mixed in equal amounts.
- Pressure through clamping or weights is essential.
- Quick-drying varieties will set in three to four hours. Heat makes the drying process quicker.

Polystyrene cement.

- Used to join rigid polystyrene such as that used on model kits.
- Dries quickly and gives a clear joint.

- Can be messy, but surplus cement can be removed with acetone.

Tensol cement.

- Used to join acrylic.
- Ready-for-use, solvent-based cement.
- Sets quickly.
- Surrounding area of joint should be masked off to avoid cement marking surface.
- Pressure is required while setting takes place.
- Precautions: good ventilation is essential when using Tensol; avoid contact with skin.

Nails

Nails on their own do not provide a permanent joint. It is the adhesive used with the nail that provides permanence. The use of nails to provide a strong wood joint is dealt with in chapter 2.

Joints in wood

Joints used in the construction of wooden products can be broadly classified into three groups: **carcase or box construction, stool construction** and **frame construction**.

Carcase or box construction

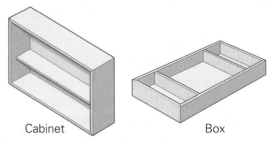

Cabinet   Box

Figure 3.87 Carcase construction

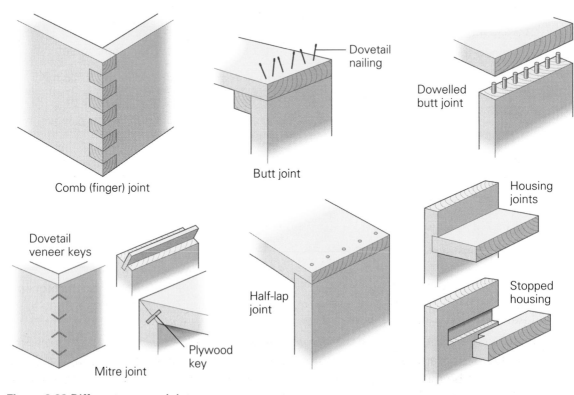

Comb (finger) joint

Butt joint

Dovetail nailing

Dowelled butt joint

Dovetail veneer keys

Mitre joint

Plywood key

Half-lap joint

Housing joints

Stopped housing

Figure 3.88 Different carcase joints

Although they are called different names, the cabinet and box are basically the same product using the same constructions.

Joints that could be used at the corners include comb (finger), butt, dowel, mitre and half-lap.

Shelves and partitions can be fitted using housing joints. It is not always necessary to reinforce the butt joint as long as it is nailed and glued. The number of dowels needed can also be reduced, depending on the size and purpose of the carcase. The purpose of the veneer keys is to reinforce the mitre joint. Without this strengthening the joint would be quite weak. Housing joints are used to fit shelves and partitions. The stopped housing looks better than the through housing since you cannot see the bottom of the housing on the front edge.

Stool construction

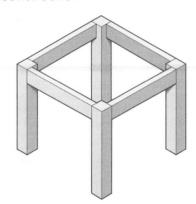

Figure 3.89 Stool construction

Stool construction is used when making small tables or stools and involves the joining of rails to legs. Joints that could be used include dowel, bridle, and mortise and tenon. Notice how, when the rails enter the leg, the ends of the tenons have to be mitred at 45 degrees so that both tenons fit properly.

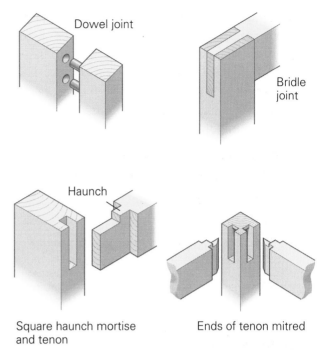

Dowel joint

Bridle joint

Haunch

Square haunch mortise and tenon

Ends of tenon mitred

Figure 3.90 Different joints used in stool construction

Frame construction

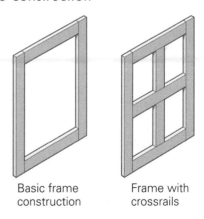

Basic frame construction

Frame with crossrails

Figure 3.91 Frame construction

Frame construction is used to make doors with panels inserted or with manufactured board covering the frame. Joints that could be used at the corners include butt, corner halving, mitre, dowel, mortise and tenon, and bridle. The butt joint can be strengthened with corner pieces or a fastener. The flush door gets its strength, not from the butt joint, but from the nails and adhesive used to fix the door panel to the frame. The cross-halving joint is used to allow both cross rails to 'cross' each other inside the frame. You can see that the dowel, mortise and tenon, and bridle joints used in stool construction could also be used in frame construction.

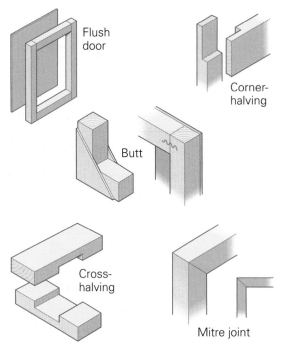

Figure 3.92 Different joints used in frame construction

Riveting

Rivets are a quick way of joining metal sheets and thin metal. You do not need to know how to rivet, but be aware of different types and where they are used.

Round or snap-head rivets are used where a countersunk or flush finish is not needed.

Countersunk head rivets are the most commonly used and provide a flush surface.

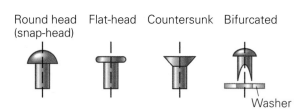

Figure 3.93 Types of rivet

Flat-head rivets are used in thin material where a countersunk is not possible.

Bifurcated rivets are used to join soft materials such as leather and plastics.

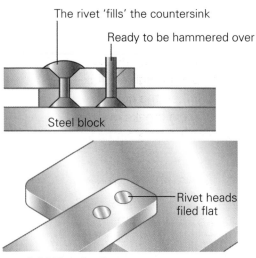

Figure 3.94 The riveting process

When using countersunk head rivets to join thin metal, the rivet would be hammered over to fill the countersink. The surplus metal would then be filed off to produce a flush finish.

Pop riveting was developed for use in the construction of aircraft. Pop riveting is used to fasten thin sheet metal and other materials. Washers can be used so that soft materials can be fastened. Because the rivets used in the pop rivet gun are hollow, they are not as strong as solid rivets.

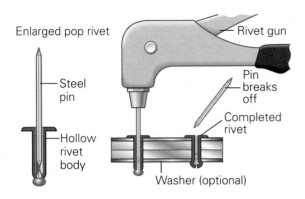

Figure 3.95 Pop riveting

Holes are first drilled through the pieces to be joined. The hollow rivet is mounted on a head pin which is pushed into the rivet gun. The rivet is pushed into the pre-drilled holes and the gun is squeezed. This has the effect of pulling the pin through and expanding the rivet head. When the correct pressure is reached, the pin breaks off, leaving the formed rivet with the pin head in it.

Heat processes to join metal

Soldering makes a permanent joint between metals by melting an alloy, with a lower melting point than the metal being joined, between the metals. Soft soldering, hard soldering and brazing are all types of soldering.

Preparation is essential for successful soldering:

1. The area of the joint must be cleaned using a file, emery cloth or steel wool. Solder will only stick to clean metal.
2. A flux is applied. The purpose of the flux is to keep the surfaces clean and prevent oxidisation when the heat is applied. In addition, the flux helps the solder flow into the joint. There are different types of flux for different situations.

Soft soldering

Soft solder is an alloy of lead and tin in varying amounts. Common uses for soft soldering include joining copper water pipes and also to solder electrical/electronic connections. Soft soldering can be carried out using a brazing torch or soldering iron because of the low melting point of the solder.

Hard soldering

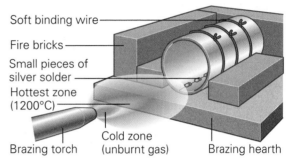

Figure 3.96 Hard soldering process

Hard soldering is also known as silver soldering because the solder is an alloy of silver, copper and zinc. The joint needs to be close-fitting and clean. Several small pieces of silver solder are cut from a strip and placed on the joint. The brazing torch is used to heat the metal gently at first, before a small hot flame is used to heat the metal to dull red. At this stage the solder will run along the joint.

Brazing

Brazing is used to join steel together by melting brazing rod between the two pieces of metal to be joined. Preparation is similar to that of soft and hard soldering. The steel is heated until red-hot and the brazing rod is placed against the join. The brazing rod melts and flows along the join. The steel is then allowed to cool without quenching.

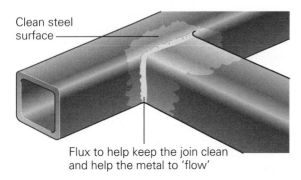

Clean steel surface

Flux to help keep the join clean and help the metal to 'flow'

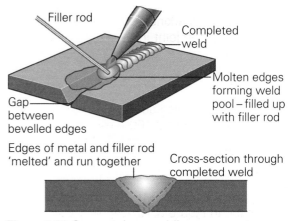

Filler rod

Completed weld

Gap between bevelled edges

Molten edges forming weld pool – filled up with filler rod

Edges of metal and filler rod 'melted' and run together

Cross-section through completed weld

Figure 3.98 Oxyacetylene welding

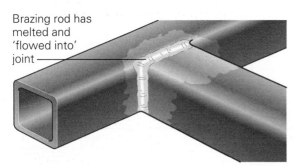

Brazing rod has melted and 'flowed into' joint

Figure 3.97 Brazing two pieces of square steel tube

Welding

Two common forms of welding are oxyacetylene and electric arc. Welding is done by applying extreme heat to the two surfaces to be joined.

The **oxyacetylene** method uses a mixture of the two gases to produce 3500 °C heat. The heat melts the two surfaces, causing a gap to develop. This gap is filled by applying a filler rod that melts into the joint and fuses the surfaces together.

The **electric arc** method uses a flux-coated filler rod that acts as an electrode. Heat is achieved by sending a low-voltage, high electrical current between the filler rod and the metals to be joined.

QUESTIONS

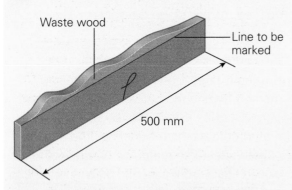

Waste wood

Line to be marked

500 mm

Figure 3.99 Length of wood marked out to be planed to width

1. Name the tools used to:
   • mark out the line
   • remove the waste wood in Figure 3.99.

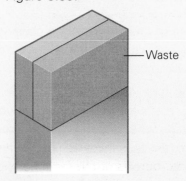

Waste

Figure 3.100

2. Name the marking-out tools used to mark out the joint in Figure 3.100 when the material is:
   • metal
   • wood.

3. Name the tools used to remove the waste in Figure 3.100 when the material is:
   • metal
   • wood.

4. Name the chisel used to complete the shape in Figure 3.101 when made from wood.

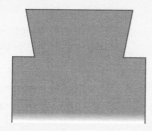

Figure 3.101 Dovetail joint

5. Name the file used to complete the shape shown in Figure 3.101 when made from metal.

6. The two components in Figure 3.102 could be made from wood, metal or plastics.
   • Name a suitable waterproof adhesive that could be used to glue the pieces of wood together.
   • Name a solvent used to glue the acrylic plastic together.
   • Name a method of joining the pieces of mild steel together permanently.
   • Name a method of joining the pieces of mild steel together temporarily.

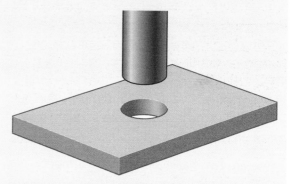

Figure 3.102 Rod and base to be joined

KEY TERMS

FABRICATING is to do with the way materials are joined together.
SOLDERING makes a permanent joint between metals by melting between the metals an alloy that has a lower melting point than the metals being joined.

Reforming processes

Casting

The casting process involves pouring liquefied material into moulds of the required shape and allowing it to solidify. It is the oldest

KEY POINT

• In reforming processes the material has to undergo a change of state, usually from solid to liquid and then back to solid. These processes are widely used in the manufacturing industry, but many are not suitable for use in schools because of restrictions involving equipment and health and safety issues. Reforming processes can be used on metals and plastics, and in some cases the processes for the two materials are very similar.

reforming process of all, and although it is usually considered as a metal-forming process, it can also be used with thermosetting plastic resins. It is perfectly possible to produce castings in the school workshop using either one of the low-melting-point metal alloys now available, or plastic casting resin. No special equipment is needed and only basic safety precautions need to be taken when working with the liquefied material.

Die-casting

Where an item can be made from a low-melting-point metal and is needed in large quantities, the die-casting process is used. The moulds (**dies**) are made from steel and are very expensive to make, but they can be used many times over and are economic for mass production of parts.

There are two basic die-casting methods: **gravity** die-casting and **pressure** die-casting. The choice of which to use is dependent on the number of castings required, the size of the castings and the amount of fine detail in the shape. Where detail and finish are not important, the gravity die-casting process is preferred as the dies and the process are simpler, the molten metal being poured in

under its own weight. Very fine detail and a good finish are possible using the pressure die-casting process, as the molten metal is forced into the parts of the dies. Typical examples of these types of castings are toy car bodies, hacksaw handles and engine casings, all of which are produced in large quantities.

KEY TERM

DIE – A steel mould that can be used many times.

Injection-moulding

Injection-moulding is a very similar process to pressure die-casting and is the most common process used for the large-scale production of **thermoplastic** parts. The moulds for injection-moulding are expensive to make, but the speed of production is high, and large quantities can be produced cheaply using **batch production** techniques. For small items, **multi-impression** moulds can be made to produce large numbers at a time, each impression being joined together to allow the plastic to flow through all parts of

Figure 3.103 Products made by die-casting

Figure 3.104 School injection-moulding machine

the mould. Moulds are produced as complete **toolsets** that can easily be removed from the injection-moulding machine and replaced with a toolset for a different product.

Figure 3.105 Industrial injection-moulding machine

Figure 3.106 Injection-moulded products

The raw material for injection-mouldings takes the form of **granules** or **pellets** of thermoplastic material fed into a storage **hopper** on the injection-moulding machine. A rotating **feed screw** takes the thermoplastic through a **heating chamber** where it is melted, ready for injection into the mould. When there is enough molten plastic in the **shot chamber**, the screw stops rotating and hydraulic pressure moves

the **ram** forward to force the plastic into the **mould**, where it cools and solidifies. The mould is then opened to release the finished mouldings and the whole process can then be repeated.

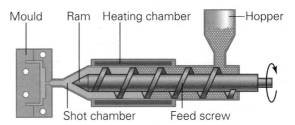

Figure 3.107 Diagram of an injection-moulding machine

Extrusion

The extrusion process is used to form lengths of uniform section by forcing molten thermoplastic through a specially shaped **die**. It is particularly useful for making products such as plastic pipes, curtain tracks, gutters and sections for window frames, using suitable thermoplastics such as polyethylene, polypropylene and PVC.

The feed system for an extrusion machine is similar to that of an injection-moulding machine, in that it uses a **feed screw** to take thermoplastic **granules** through a heating chamber. In the case of the extrusion machine, however, the feed screw rotates continuously to force the molten material through the die, and no hydraulic ram is needed. Some extrusion machines now use compressed air to feed the material instead of a feed screw, so that much higher extrusion speeds can be achieved for mass production. The extruded section cools after leaving the die and is either cut into suitable lengths or rolled into coils.

The extrusion process is often combined with **blow-moulding** on special machines used to produce bottles of all shapes and sizes. A length of extruded tube is fed directly into a heated bottle mould, where it is cut off and clamped between the two mould halves. Air is then blown in to force the plastic against the sides of the hot mould and form the shape of the bottle. The mould is then opened to release the finished bottle and the process is repeated on a continuous flow-line principle.

KEY POINT

- All forming processes for thermoplastics require the plastic to be softened by heat, and the processes are collectively referred to as **thermoforming** processes.

The machine shown in figure 3.109 can be used to demonstrate six different thermoforming processes, and includes an oven that can be used to heat sheets of plastic for press-moulding and drape-forming.

Figure 3.109 A thermoforming centre

GRP-moulding

KEY POINT

- **Glass-reinforced plastic** (GRP) is often referred to as 'fibreglass' and is produced by **laminating** layers of stranded glass-fibre matting in **polyester resin**, which is a thermosetting plastic.

The liquid resin used in GRP-moulding is reinforced by the glass matting and is hardened by the heat produced by an

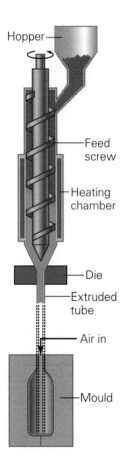

Figure 3.108 Diagram of a combined extrusion/blow-moulding machine

exothermic reaction that takes place as the resin gels. The resulting material has a high strength-to-weight ratio and good impact resistance, making it suitable for a wide range of applications, from simple trays to boat hulls and car bodies. Quite complex curved shapes can be formed using inexpensive moulds, making the process very useful for the small-scale production of large items and also for prototypes of new products. Further developments of the process include the use of carbon fibre and Kevlar™ as reinforcement, either instead of or combined with glass fibre; very strong lightweight structures can be moulded in this way.

The size and shape of the front section of the railway locomotive in figure 3.110 make it ideal for making as a GRP-moulding, particularly as it needs to be light and only a fairly small number will be made.

Figure 3.110 GRP-moulding

The moulds for GRP-moulding can be made from almost any material, including wood, MDF, plywood, sheet metal and plaster of Paris, and when moulds are likely to be used many times, they are often made from GRP itself. As with all types of moulds, the most important feature is that the finished

moulding should be easy to remove, and tapered sides, rounded corners and smooth surfaces are all vital in the design of the item to be produced and the making of the mould to produce it. The final surface of the mould must be sealed, waxed and highly polished before it can be used for the laying-up of a GRP moulding.

Figure 3.111 shows the two types of mould used: male moulds and female moulds. Because the surface formed against the mould is smooth but the outer surface is not, the type of mould needs to be chosen carefully.

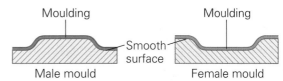

Figure 3.111 Male and female moulds

A boat hull would be moulded using a female mould because the outer surface of the hull is visible and needs to have a good finish. The simple tray shown in figure 3.112 is produced on a male mould to make the inner surface of the tray smooth and easy to wipe clean.

When making a GRP-moulding, a number of precautions need to be taken to ensure it is done safely. A visor and gloves should be worn so that there is no possibility of resin getting onto the skin or in the eyes, and good ventilation and extraction is needed to remove the fumes given off by the resins.

To make a GRP-moulding, the mould must first be polished and cleaned, before applying a coat of release agent to make it easy to remove the finished moulding. When the

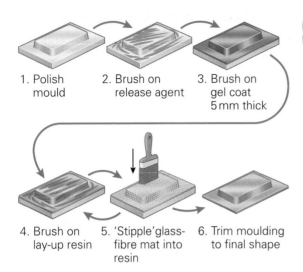

1. Polish mould

2. Brush on release agent

3. Brush on gel coat 5mm thick

4. Brush on lay-up resin

5. 'Stipple' glass-fibre mat into resin

6. Trim moulding to final shape

Figure 3.112 GRP-moulding

release agent is fully dried, **gel-coat resin** is mixed with the correct amount of liquid **catalyst** and brushed onto the mould to a thickness of about 5 mm. The gel coat is normally coloured with pigment to give what is called a **self-coloured** moulding that does not need painting.

The gel coat is left to harden (gel) until it is just slightly tacky, which takes about 15–30 minutes, depending on the thickness. **Lay-up resin** is then mixed with catalyst and brushed over the gel coat to give an even layer of about 2 mm thickness. The **glass-fibre matting** should be cut into manageable-sized strips and pressed into the lay-up resin all over the mould. It is very important that all of the glass-fibre mat is soaked in resin to give a strong moulding, and that the mat is **stippled** into the resin with a brush or rolled with a special aluminium laminating roller to remove any air bubbles. The 'laying-up' process is repeated to build up the required thickness of moulding before being left to fully 'cure', which takes several days.

Systems and control

The type of 'system' includes jigs, fixtures, templates and patterns, which are all used to control accuracy when manufacturing products in quantity. They can also be used to control accuracy in the manufacture of single products if the product has a number of identical components. There is a subtle difference between a jig and a fixture. Technically, a jig is used to guide a tool, for example, a drill or saw, while a fixture is the means of holding the work in place. Some examples of jigs, formers and templates with specific uses are shown below.

Jigs

Jigs are 3D devices that can be used to assist the manufacturing process when sawing, drilling, bending and shaping.

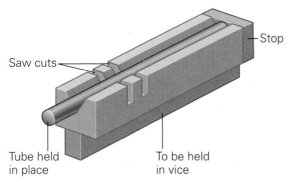

Figure 3.113 Sawing jig

The **sawing jig** has the following good features:

- The tube to be cut is held securely in place.
- Part of the jig can fit into a vice to prevent it from moving about.
- Identical lengths can be sawn, due to the position of the saw cuts.
- It is straightforward to use.

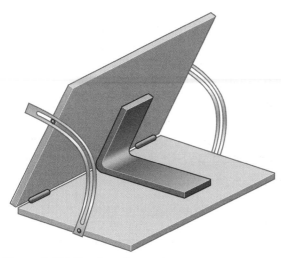

Figure 3.114 Bending jig

The **bending jig**, used to produce the internal bend in the sheet plastic, has the following good features:

- It is adjustable to any angle between 0 and 90 degrees.

- It can be adjusted quickly and easily.
- The plastic can be pushed into the angle easily.
- The same angle can be achieved every time.

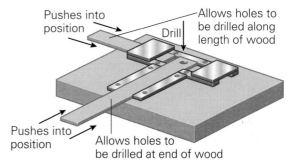

Figure 3.115 Drilling jig

The **drilling jig** has the following good features:

- The jig fits quickly and easily over a drilling machine table.
- Strips of wood can be pushed into the jig and are held safely while being drilled.
- The holes can be drilled at the end of a strip or along its length, depending on which 'guide' is used.
- The holes will be drilled in the same place every time.

Templates

Templates are the best way to mark out irregular or awkward shapes. Any thin, fairly rigid material is suitable. Thick card, for example, could be used to mark a small batch of products. If the scale of manufacture was larger, then a more durable material such as manufactured board or thin metal sheet would be better.

Using a template, a shape can be marked out quickly and accurately on sheet material. Some templates require greater accuracy, for example, when marking out positions for constructions. In this case, it would be essential for the template to have some form of lipping that fitted up against at least two edges, to ensure the correct location every time.

Patterns

If you were to cut out an ornate part of some stage scenery from a sheet of plywood, it would be easier to cut the shape out of paper or thin card first and then glue it onto the plywood. You could then use the pattern to give you the outline of the shape required.

KEY TERM

JIGS are 3D devices that can be used to assist the manufacturing process when sawing, drilling, bending and shaping.

3.2 KNOWLEDGE AND UNDERSTANDING OF BASIC EQUIPMENT

Imagine a workshop situation. Your teacher asks you to get a length of mild steel tube from the storeroom and cut off a piece 400 mm long. You have learnt about measuring, marking out and sawing different materials during your design and technology course, and now is the time to put it into practice. You should be able to:

- know which tools you need and recognise them;
- name the tools;
- use them safely and effectively.

In addition, you should be able to carry out a similar task, but on a length of 50 × 25 mm pine.

EXAMINER'S TIPS

Examiners often ask students to name tools and equipment they would use to carry out a specific task. They also expect you to describe the safety precautions associated with those tools and equipment.

3.3 AWARENESS OF ALTERNATIVE TOOLS AND EQUIPMENT

Think about the previous example of sawing a length of 50 × 25 mm pine. You correctly named a tenon saw and you held the work securely against a bench stop. But there are alternative methods: you could have taken the length of pine to a Hegner saw and cut it quickly and accurately.

Think about the different ways of removing metal: using a cold chisel, hacksaw or even bench shears, depending on the size of the material.

EXAMINER'S TIPS

Examiners often ask students to describe two methods of carrying out the same task. Sometimes they may require an answer that describes a 'hand' method and a 'machine' method.

3.4 SAFETY CHECKS TO CARRY OUT ON ELECTRICAL EQUIPMENT

Always be aware of the potential dangers in your workshop. For example, portable electrical equipment needs to be robust and well maintained due to the nature of its use. Always check the equipment visually for obvious dangers, such as frayed or damaged cable on electrical soldering irons or drills. Make sure that there are no loose screws on plugs. If you are in any doubt, do not use the equipment, and inform your teacher of your concerns.

3.5 MACHINE SETTINGS AND CHECKS

There are a number of settings and checks that are common to drilling machines, centre lathes and milling machines and which should be carried out every time the machine is used.

Always make sure that:

- the workpiece is held securely in a chuck or vice;
- the correct drill, lathe tool or milling cutter is selected and that it is in good condition;
- the drill, lathe tool or milling cutter is held securely in the chuck, arbor or spindle;
- the correct speed is set in terms of the size of the drill, tool or cutter used and the material to be cut;
- chuck keys are removed before switching on;
- guards are in place and eye protection is worn.

CHAPTER 4

COMPUTER APPLICATIONS

By the end of this chapter you should have developed a knowledge and understanding of:

- the use of CAD packages in school
- on-screen modelling
- appropriate use of text, database and graphics software
- the storage and sharing of data electronically
- practical applications of CAD/CAM
- CNC (computer numerical control) machines.

This chapter is concerned with the use of computers to help you when you are involved in the practical activities of designing and making. It is to do with designing, drawing, word-processing, modelling and making. Much of the chapter will concentrate on the two important areas of CAD (computer-aided design) and CAM (computer-aided manufacture). It will look at software that enables you to design in 2D and 3D, and machines that can transfer your designs into 3D working products. Although this is important to your practical work and you will be expected to use CAD/CAM in Units 1 and 3, examiners may also ask questions about CAD/CAM in the written papers, and you need to know what the benefits of using CAD/CAM are.

4.1 USE OF CAD PACKAGES IN SCHOOL

Two-dimensional CAD software packages such as TechSoft 2D Design V2 are straightforward to use and offer many features that allow you to produce different types of design drawings. Not only can you draw, design and model on-screen, but with your computer linked to a compatible machine, you can actually see your product made by the machine.

- You can produce accurate, fully dimensioned 'technical drawings'.
- You can create manufacturing drawings

that can then be outputted to a variety of CAM devices such as vinyl cutters, plotter/engravers, millers, routers and laser cutters.

- You can undertake graphic design activity, allowing you to combine vector graphics, text, bitmap images, photographs and Clip Art to create and manipulate images for items such as logos, menus, point-of-sale display and product packaging.

Three-dimensional CAD packages such as SolidWorks® give you the opportunity to develop working drawings that include both 2D and 3D images of your design ideas. These can be analysed and amended on-screen. In addition, you can also generate outstanding, professional presentation drawings.

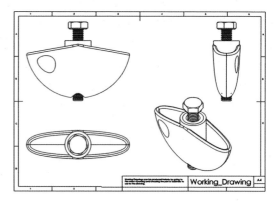

Figure 4.3 Working drawings

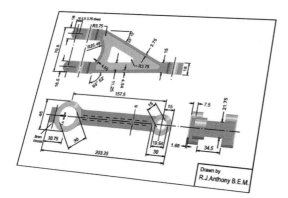

Figure 4.1 Technical drawing produced using 2D Design V2

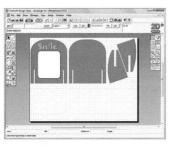

Figure 4.2 2D Design V2 – manufacturing drawings for photo frame and final product

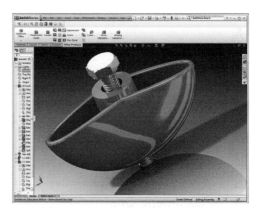

Figure 4.4 Presentation drawing

4.2 ON-SCREEN MODELLING AND IMAGE MANIPULATION

Most software allows you to cleverly control the drawings you produce on-screen. Features include the ability to zoom in on drawings or to rotate in order to view the drawing from all angles. The 2D Design V2

program gives you the opportunity to convert drawings from bitmap images such as JPEG files into vector paths. This means that drawings you have made by hand or scanned can be converted on-screen. This, in turn, means that they could provide the paths to be cut or engraved by machines connected to the computer. Drawings can be rendered to produce photorealistic images. Software enables you to determine the lighting effects, the material and texture and even background scenery. Some software includes automated assembly, using nuts, bolts, screws and other components. Animation means that it is possible to see an accurate moving image of a design.

On a single sheet it is possible to produce working drawings, a presentation drawing and manufacturing drawings. It is vital that you invest a portion of your time trying out some of the features that the software offers.

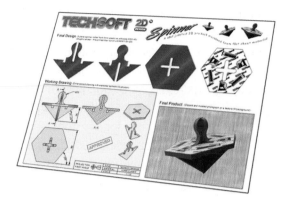

Figure 4.5 Spinner drawings

4.3 TEXT, DATABASE AND GRAPHICS SOFTWARE

Text, or word-processing, software was originally designed just to produce text documents, but many of the programs available now are very versatile and can be used in a number of ways. The most commonly used word-processing program is Microsoft® **Word**. This is not only used to produce text, it also allows tables and simple drawings to be created, and material to be **pasted in** from other programs to add to and illustrate a document. One really useful feature of word-processing programs is the fact that they offer spelling and grammar checks and provide on-screen reminders of when these checks are needed.

Most word-processing packages come with a selection of **Clip Art**, which is the name given to files of pre-prepared pictures that can be used in the text. To find a Clip Art

picture, click on the **Insert** menu and select **Picture** and then **Clip Art**. When you have found a suitable picture, click on it to insert it into your document and then move, enlarge or reduce it by using the mouse.

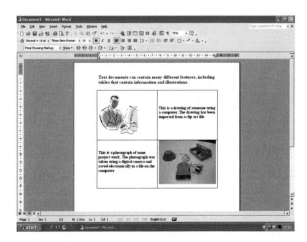

Figure 4.6 An illustrated text document

Databases are used to store and process information, and each piece of data is referred to as an **entry** on the database. A telephone directory is an example of a database, but computerised databases are much more useful as they can be used to access information very quickly. As well as storing a lot of information, you can also use the database to add to, delete or modify the information when required, without affecting the rest of the entries.

Most computerised databases have Sort and Filter functions to allow you to rearrange the information into different orders or groups. The example shown in figure 4.7 is a database with details of the tools needed in a school workshop. The **Sort** function could be used to rearrange the tools on the database into alphabetical order, and the **Filter** function could give a list of the tools in a particular cupboard number for stock checking.

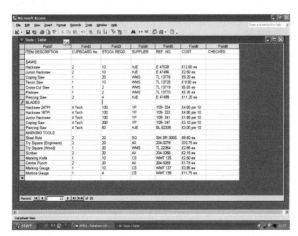

Figure 4.7 Example of a database

Spreadsheets are quite similar to databases because they look like tables of information, but they are able to perform other functions in addition to storing and sorting information. A spreadsheet allows you to enter text and numbers into a table and then carry out calculations on them. They can be used to

help calculate the total cost of a project by entering details of all the things needed and how much each one costs.

One of the most common programs used for spreadsheets is Microsoft Excel®, which also allows charts to be produced to present the data on the spreadsheet graphically. Once the spreadsheet has been produced, a **Chart Wizard** is used to draw whichever type of chart is needed to display the information. Different types of charts can be produced, and you can use this function to help present the results of surveys you might do in your project work.

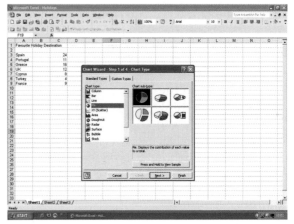

Figure 4.8 Spreadsheet and Chart Wizard

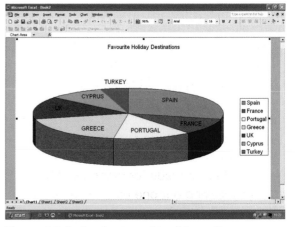

Figure 4.9 A pie chart produced from the spreadsheet

In the example shown in figure 4.8, a group of people have been asked to say what their favourite holiday destination is. The results of the survey have been put onto a spreadsheet and the Chart Wizard function has then been used to present the information in a pie chart.

ACTIVITY

1. Carry out a simple survey in your group to find out the group members' favourite colour or type of music.

2. Enter the results of your survey onto a spreadsheet and produce a chart to present the results graphically.

3. Try out the different types of charts available on the Wizard and decide which you think presents the information in the clearest form.

4. When you have decided on the type of chart to use, produce a fully labelled version and keep a copy of the spreadsheet and the chart in your folder.

Spreadsheets are used a lot by businesses to help calculate their costs and profits. Relevant data is usually transferred from a database to produce a spreadsheet for a particular purpose, and the spreadsheet software then allows the user to see what effects any changes to the data would have. They could calculate how much an increase in the cost of one part would reduce the amount of profit made, or what could be saved by leaving out one part, such as using only three screws instead of four for assembling a product.

Graphics software packages come in many forms, ranging from simple collections of Clip Art to complex packages that allow 3D modelling and animation to be carried out. The software that you use at school or college will depend on what is available on the network, but many of the packages can be used on your home PC or laptop.

When using CAD packages to produce drawings, it is best to choose the program that is most suitable for what you want to draw. Do not be tempted to use a powerful 3D CAD package when the drawing you want

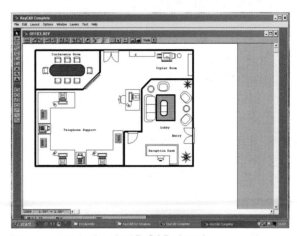

Figure 4.10 A simple 2D CAD drawing

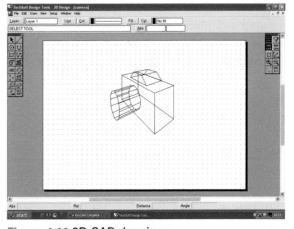

Figure 4.11 3D CAD drawing

to produce can be drawn more easily and quickly on an alternative program, such as Techsoft 2D Design. All that really matters is that the drawing you produce is clear and shows what you want it to show.

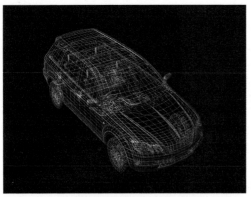

Figure 4.12 3D CAD drawing of a car

KEY TERMS

CLIP ART – Files of ready-prepared drawings.
DATABASE – A document for storing and processing information (data).
SPREADSHEET – Text and numbers contained in a table allowing calculations to be carried out.
WIZARD – Part of a program that helps perform a particular function.
GRAPHICS SOFTWARE – Computer programs to produce drawings.

4.4 STORING AND SHARING DATA

KEY POINT

• As the amount of data produced and used on computers increases, so the need for this data to be stored in large amounts becomes more important. The size of any storage device is referred to by how much **memory** it has, and items such as photographs from digital cameras and drawings from CAD packages take up a lot of memory, particularly when compared with simple text documents. Most data is normally stored on the **hard drive** of a PC or the **server** of a network, but with the increasing use of laptops, notebooks and PDAs (personal digital assistants), more portable storage devices have been developed to allow important files to be carried around and shared between individual machines.

The amount of memory needed is determined by the file size, measured in **bytes** and usually expressed as a number of **kilobytes** or **megabytes**.

• 1 kilobyte (KB) = 1000 bytes
• 1 megabyte (MB) = 1 million bytes
• 1 gigabyte (GB) = 1000 million bytes
• 1 terabyte (TB) = 1 million million bytes

Some examples of typical file sizes are:

• a page of text – 30 KB
• a simple CAD drawing – 200 KB
• a high-resolution photograph – 20 MB.

Some computers still have the facility to use a **floppy disk**, which normally has a capacity of 1.44 MB, meaning that it could store about seven CAD drawings, but would not be big enough for even one high-resolution photograph. Although these floppy disks are no longer used, external floppy disk drives are available to connect to the computer through a **USB** port, allowing the old disks to be used to transfer the files to another device.

Floppy disks were replaced some time ago by the **CD-ROM**, which has a capacity of 700 MB and could therefore store over 30 high-resolution photographs. More recently, **DVDs** were introduced, and although these are normally associated with films, they can also be used in the same way as CDs, but are capable of storing much more data.

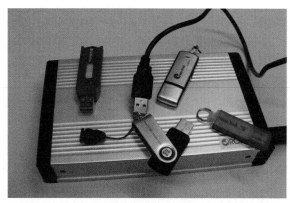

Figure 4.13 Memory sticks and external hard drive

Memory sticks are very widely used to store data and their capacity is increasing all the time. These devices are also referred to as pen drives and flash drives, and capacities of 8 GB and more are not uncommon. Not only are these devices small and convenient to carry around, but files can easily be deleted from them, unlike the CD-ROM with its **read-only memory**.

External hard drives can be connected through a USB port to increase the memory and improve the speed of a computer, and these are now being made so much smaller in physical size that they are easily carried in a pocket. The trend is to increase the capacity and reduce the size of storage devices so that more and more information can be conveniently stored and carried around.

Data that is stored electronically is very easy to share with other people in a number of ways, and one of the most widely used methods is the internet. Information can be

put onto a website so that it can be downloaded by anyone, or it can be sent electronically to individuals as attachments to emails. Because storage devices are physically small but able to hold large amounts of data, the devices themselves can be sent by secure delivery methods to prevent important data being accessed illegally.

KEY TERMS

USB – Universal serial bus, used to connect external devices to the computer.
CD-ROM – A compact disk storage device with read-only memory.
MEMORY STICK – (pen drive) Storage device connected to a computer through a USB port.
EXTERNAL HARD DRIVE – Portable storage device with large capacity.

4.5 APPLICATIONS OF CAD/CAM

Designing and making of models and prototypes

On-screen models can help you to visualise what the final product will look like. Prototype models can be made by downloading data from your computer images to a machine that can reproduce the design exactly.

Rapid prototyping is the manufacture of a replica model of a final product, the only difference being the material in which the model is made. The term 'rapid' describes the speed with which the model is manufactured, compared with the final actual product made from resistant materials.

Commercial rapid prototyping involves the building up of layers of material to achieve the shape, but it is possible to use machines in school that use a milling cutter to remove material from a block to achieve the finished shape of a product.

Figure 4.15 Prototype model

  EXAMINER'S TIPS

CAM can help you to achieve a high-quality product. Projects where CAM is used to complete part of the product are the best as far as assessment of your work is concerned in Units 1 and 3. This is because it is vital that you are able to demonstrate a range of skills, other than CAM, in the products you make. A project to design and make an educational toy can involve the design and manufacture of the vinyl letters to go on the blocks.

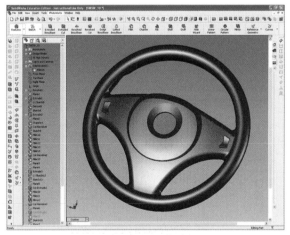

Figure 4.14 On-screen modelling

Figure 4.16 Letter blocks

Figure 4.18 Alphabet letters

This could be done by designing the letters on-screen. You could try different types of font, different sizes and colours to match the vinyl you will make them from. Then download the design data from your computer to a machine such as a Roland CAMM1 vinyl cutter. This would produce excellent letters which could then be peeled off a backing sheet and stuck onto the wooden blocks.

Having designed the letters on-screen, these could be made using either a laser cutter (shown in Figure 4.19) or a miller/router (shown in Figure 4.20).

Figure 4.19 Laser CAMM A2

Figure 4.17 Roland CAMM 1 GX24

Another educational toy could be manufactured totally using CAD/CAM.

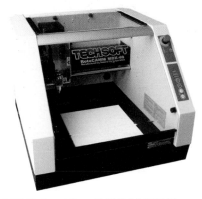

Figure 4.20 Roland RotoCAMM MDX40

❭ Benefits of CAD/CAM

EXAMINER'S TIPS

When asked an examination question about the benefits of CAD/CAM, many students simply state 'quicker', 'faster', 'accurate' and receive no marks. Try to write a sentence that describes clearly a specific benefit, as in the examples below.

CAD:
- Computers can be used to make changes to a design and edit it without having to redraw it.
- Computers can be used to produce very accurate drawings and dimension exactly to what is drawn.
- Computers can produce photorealistic models without having to make them.
- Computers can show or simulate how a product will behave without having to undertake expensive testing.

CAM:
- Computers do not make mistakes if programmed properly.
- Computers give reliable and consistently high standards of manufacture.
- Computers achieve quicker production times. Complex shapes and designs can be created easily.

KEY TERM

RAPID PROTOTYPING is the manufacture of a replica model of a final product.

❭ One-off and quantity production

KEY POINT

- CAD/CAM refers to the use of computer software to help in the designing and making of a product. A program with details of the design produced by CAD is transferred to a CAM machine for the product to be made. The CAM element of CAD/CAM can relate to the production of a single prototype or to the quantity manufacture of a final product.

The designing and modelling of a product is done as a 'one-off' production operation (see chapter 5) and any changes to the design that are required are made while the final prototype is developed. Once the software program has been finalised, it can then be used to make the product in whatever quantity is needed. The CAM machines that you use in school are really only designed to make products on a one-off basis, but small quantities of identical products (batches) can be produced by using specially made **fixtures** to position the work on the machines.

When producing very large quantities of products on an industrial scale, automated systems are used for positioning and clamping work on machines so that they can work more quickly. Machines are also often linked together as part of a completely automatic production line, and these systems are discussed in more detail in chapter 5.

4.6 COMPUTER NUMERICAL CONTROL (CNC) MACHINES

KEY POINT

- Any machine that is controlled by a computer is a CNC machine because all computer control is numerical.

To make a part on a CNC machine, a program is needed to control the movement of the cutting tool in relation to the material being cut. The program is usually imported direct from a suitable CAD package as part of the whole CAD/CAM process.

In the case of a CNC lathe, the program controls the movement of the cutting tools, but on a CNC router or milling machine the program controls the movement of the machine table as well as the vertical movement of the cutting tool. When a number of different cutting tools are needed to complete the part, the program makes sure that the correct tool is selected and positioned for each operation.

Laser cutting machines do not have 'tools' in the usual sense of the word, but control of the machine is the same as for a CNC router or milling machine, with the movement of the laser beam being computer-controlled (see chapter 3).

Figure 4.22 **CNC milling machine**

Figure 4.23 **Parts made by CNC machining**

CNC machines that are used in industry are much larger and more powerful than the ones you may see in school. CNC lathes, laser cutters, routers and milling machines are all widely used, and machines are also made to be able to carry out many different processes. A typical CNC **machining centre**

Figure 4.21 **CNC lathe for training use**

used in a factory will be able to carry out turning, drilling, milling and boring, and would have tool storage for all the necessary tools to carry out these operations, and a turret for changing the tools when necessary.

KEY TERMS

FIXTURE – A specially made device for holding parts to be machined. It is 'fixed' onto the machine to hold the part securely.
CNC – (computer numerical control) Controlled by computer.
MACHINING CENTRE – A machine that can carry out different operations.

Figure 4.24 Industrial CNC machine

CHAPTER 5

INDUSTRIAL PRODUCTION

By the end of this chapter you should have developed a knowledge and understanding of:

- basic commercial production methods and how they are applied to the manufacture of products
- factors affecting the choice of production method to be used
- the impact of new technologies on industrial production
- commercial manufacturing systems and their application to quantity production
- the impact of globalisation on industry, society and the environment.

LEARNING OUTCOMES

This chapter deals with how industry works, and how the processes we covered in chapter 3 are applied to the commercial manufacture of products on a large scale. Because improvements in manufacturing technology are constantly being made, many of the methods and systems we look at may be modified or combined to suit particular situations, especially when the scale of production is very high. Manufacturers have to ensure that their products are made as efficiently and as cheaply as possible, and this often leads to systems being developed specifically for one particular product.

5.1 COMMERCIAL PRODUCTION METHODS

Methods should not be confused with processes. What we do to a material in order to make something is called a process, but a method is how we apply that process to manufacture one or more products. The three basic production methods are generally referred to as:

- **one-off production** – sometimes called 'job' production and used for one or a small number of products
- **batch production** – used to produce a specified quantity of identical products (the number of products in the 'batch' is

dependent on many factors, but the batch can be repeated when required)

- **high-volume production** – producing very large numbers of one type of product (the products involved may or may not be identical in every way).

KEY POINT

- The choice of production method to be used is based on the type of product and the quantity to be made.

One-off production

As the name suggests, this method is normally used where only one product is to be specially made, and most of the project work you do in the school workshop will be done in this way. It can also be applied when a small number of products are needed, when it would be too expensive to make special tools to produce them. One-off production is very time-consuming and **labour-intensive**, often needing highly skilled workers to make all or part of the product, and this makes it an expensive method of production. One advantage of one-off

Figure 5.1 A 'one-off' product

production is that the product is unique and 'hand-made', which is usually taken as signifying that it is of higher quality than products made in large quantities. Examples of everyday products made by the one-off production method include individually designed jewellery, 'hand-crafted' decorative items and furniture, and very large products like boats and buildings.

Batch production

Batch production is used where a number of identical products are made, and special tools are normally used to make them. The size of a **batch** of products can be anything from ten to many thousands, depending on a number of factors, but batches can be repeated at any time to make more of the same product.

We can work on a type of batch production in the school workshop by allocating particular tasks to different members of a 'team'. To make a batch of simple metal nameplates, for instance, a team of four people could divide up the tasks as follows:

- mark out the shape of the nameplate – team member A
- saw off the nameplate blank – team member B
- file the nameplate to shape – team members C and D (two because it takes longer to do)
- drill the holes in the nameplate – team member A (having done all the marking out).

In this way, a 'batch' of nameplates could be made more quickly than if the team members carried out all the tasks individually.

In industry, batch production is the most widely used production method and virtually all component parts for products are made in this way. Production processes such as injection-moulding, extrusion, presswork and die-casting lend themselves well to batch production, as the tools for making a particular part are made as a self-contained unit (**toolset**). The tools for making one part can be removed from the machine and replaced by a different set of tools quite easily, so one machine can produce many different parts. The toolsets are carefully stored and maintained to use for further batches, and can produce many thousands of identical parts as and when required. Even though the tools cost a lot to make, that cost is spread over the total number of parts made, so the more parts that are made, the cheaper each part can be.

Figure 5.2 Tools for batch production

Table 5.1 shows how the cost of making parts goes down as the number of parts made increases. This is usually referred to as the **economy of scale**. The **fixed cost** is the cost of making the tools and fitting them into the machine, and the **variable cost** is the cost of actually making the parts, including material, labour and energy costs. The batch production method is used for a very wide range of products including plastic bottles, 'flat-pack' kitchen furniture, baths, tools and wheels for cars. In addition to this, virtually all the component parts used to make products by high-volume production methods are made by batch production.

High-volume production

This is sometimes referred to as **mass production** and it deals with the high-volume manufacture of products that may or may not be identical. A lot of specialist equipment is needed and it is very expensive to set up for this type of production, meaning that it is only possible to use it if large numbers of products are to be made. The cost of all the special tooling and equipment is offset by the speed and efficiency of production and the fact that only a few skilled workers are needed.

Typical examples of the high-volume production method of manufacture are cars, televisions and domestic appliances such as washing machines. These are produced on automated assembly lines, using computer-controlled handling systems to move materials and component parts, and robots to perform

Number of parts made	1000	2000	5000	10,000
Fixed cost (£)	2000	2000	2000	2000
Variable cost (£) @ 50p per part	500	1000	2500	5000
Total cost (£)	2500	3000	4500	7000
Cost per part (£)	2.50	1.50	0.90	0.70

Table 5.1 Economy of scale

Figure 5.3 A production line

the operations needed to make the product. The system allows slight differences between products to be made during their manufacture, such as different upholstery in a car or a more complex programmer in a washing machine. The computer controlling the system ensures that the right parts required for the product are supplied for assembly at the right time.

KEY TERMS

ONE-OFF PRODUCTION – Making only one or a small number of products.
BATCH PRODUCTION – Making a set number of identical products.
HIGH-VOLUME PRODUCTION – Producing very large numbers (mass production).

ACTIVITY

Cut off ten pieces of wood about 20 mm thick (the length and width do not matter). Make a simple jig out of angle iron for drilling two dowel holes in the edge of the piece of wood.

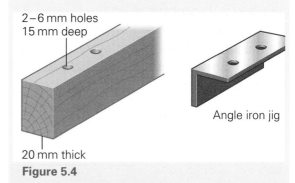

2–6 mm holes 15 mm deep

Angle iron jig

20 mm thick

Figure 5.4

Mark out and drill the two dowel holes in five of the pieces of wood and time how long it takes. Use the jig to drill the two dowel holes in the other five pieces of wood, timing how long it takes.

1. Which five pieces took the least time? Explain why.

2. Which five pieces were done most accurately? Explain why.

5.2 THE IMPACT OF NEW TECHNOLOGIES

KEY POINT

- New technologies such as CAD/CAM, rapid prototyping and computer-controlled machines have enabled products to be developed and produced more quickly.

Industrial applications of CAD/CAM

The basic principles of CAD/CAM have been dealt with in chapter 4, but these have been developed further for use in industrial production. The use of CAD/CAM in the design and development of new products has resulted in the products coming into production in much less time than was the case using more traditional techniques. On-screen modelling and rapid prototyping, together with the ability to make changes easily, are used to develop the design quickly. When the final design is chosen, the special tools such as moulds and dies needed to manufacture the product are made directly from the CAD package. All the design details can be shared electronically with companies around the world, enabling the CAM function to be performed wherever the product is to be manufactured.

Instead of using separate machines such as lathes, routers and milling machines for all the manufacturing processes, multipurpose machines have been developed that can carry out many different operations. These machines are usually referred to as **machining centres** and are computer-controlled, often as part of a fully integrated manufacturing system.

▶ Rapid prototyping

CAD packages allow the designer to view a 3D image of a new design on-screen, and a number of systems are now available for converting computer-generated designs into solid 3D models. These systems are referred to as **rapid prototyping** systems, all being computer-controlled and most being fully automatic. The 3D design is first divided up by computer software into thin horizontal 'layers'. These layers are then sent in sequence to the rapid prototyping system, where the solid model is built up layer by layer.

The 3D models are produced in a number of different ways:

Laminating – One of the earliest systems uses a vinyl cutter to cut individual layers out of adhesive-backed card. The layers are then stuck together to produce the solid model, which can be trimmed and painted to provide the finished prototype. Although the process is rather time-consuming, it can be done quite cheaply and can produce models that would be very difficult to make in any other way.

3D printing – This system works in a similar way to an inkjet printer and builds up a 3D model by 'printing' the layers onto the bed of the machine, using either molten ABS plastic, powder or wax. The 'print head' is computer-controlled to trace out the shape of the 3D model layer; and when the first layer has been printed, the bed of the machine is lowered by an amount equal to the thickness of each layer. The process is then repeated for all the remaining layers until the complete object has been produced.

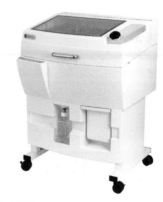

Figure 5.5 A 3D printer

The materials used in 3D printing have been developed to enable stronger, fully functioning prototypes to be produced. With continuing developments in materials and processes, 3D printing can be used for the rapid manufacture of products on a one-off or small-batch basis.

Stereolithography – This system is widely used in industry to produce good-quality prototypes from liquid plastic resin. The stereolithography machine consists of a tank of liquid resin, a movable platform on which to build the prototype and a computer-guided **laser**. The laser traces out the shape of a layer of the 3D design onto the surface of the liquid resin in the tank. This cures the resin to the shape required and the platform is then lowered to enable the next layer to be cured on top of the previous one. The process is repeated until all the layers have been cured, to produce the completed 3D prototype.

Laser-sintering – This works in a similar way to stereolithography, but the raw material is a fine, heat-fusible powder, rather than a liquid. The computer-guided laser fuses the surface of the powder in the shape of one layer of the 3D design, and this process is repeated until the prototype is completed, lowering the platform after each layer. The powders used may be plastic, metal, ceramic or a combination of these, which allows prototypes with good impact strength and thermal resistance to be produced.

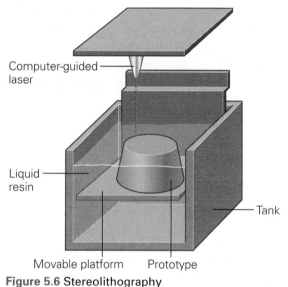

Computer-guided laser
Liquid resin
Tank
Movable platform   Prototype

Figure 5.6 Stereolithography

KEY TERMS

RAPID PROTOTYPING – Making a 3D prototype in layers by computer control.

3D PRINTER – A printer that makes 3D prototypes out of molten plastic or wax.

STEREOLITHOGRAPHY – Making 3D prototypes by curing liquid resin with a laser.

LASER-SINTERING – Using a laser to fuse fine powders in layers to make a 3D prototype.

5.3 GLOBALISATION

KEY POINT

- With ever-improving transport and communication links, it is often said that the world is getting smaller. Not only has this allowed manufacturers to sell their products around the world, but it has also enabled them to take advantage of social and economic differences between countries. Many large organisations have become **multinational companies**, with factories around the world, where their production facilities can be close to the required raw materials and can also make use of the cheap labour available.

In recent years it has become increasingly common for companies to transfer their production to other countries so that manufacturers can make their products more cheaply, and in some cases whole factories have been moved to a different country. This has led to a decline in manufacturing in countries such as the UK and Germany, and the rapid **industrialisation** of previously underdeveloped countries in other parts of the world.

In some cases, the cost of labour is not as important as logistical considerations, and many large companies have built new factories in other countries in order to make their products closer to the market they are to be sold in. Examples of this are the Japanese-owned Nissan factory in Sunderland and the Toyota factory in Derby, where vehicles are produced mainly for the European market.

While globalisation is felt to be beneficial both socially and economically, there are concerns about the treatment of workers in the 'emerging economies', particularly with regard to the use of young children in manufacturing, and the amount that workers are paid.

Another major concern is the **environmental impact** of transporting materials and goods around the world, and heavily loaded container ships, like the one in figure 5.7, are a familiar sight in every major shipping port.

Figure 5.7 Container ship

KEY TERMS

MULTINATIONAL COMPANY – A company that operates in many different countries.

INDUSTRIALISATION – Increasing the amount of manufacturing carried out in an area or country.

ENVIRONMENTAL IMPACT – The effects of manufacturing on the environment.

HEALTH AND SAFETY

By the end of this chapter you should have developed a knowledge and understanding of:

- the responsibilities of designers to ensure that products are safe to manufacture and safe in use
- the importance of personal safety when designing and making products in school workshops
- risk assessment
- COSHH
- how safety signs and symbols are used in the workshops.

This chapter deals with health and safety from the standpoint of the designer and the manufacturer. It will also focus on several important issues that you need to consider carefully when carrying out practical work in your school workshops.

6.1 DESIGNER RESPONSIBILITIES

When products are designed and manufactured it is important that they are safe to make and safe to use.

Health and safety is concerned with the well-being of everyone involved with the products during their manufacture and with consumers who purchase the products and use them.

- Products must be able to withstand misuse; for example, a child's toy that falls apart when it is accidentally dropped could be dangerous to the child. Therefore it is important to consider the choice of materials, construction or manufacturing processes and the finish that is applied to the toy.

- Products must conform to safety standards in all countries where they are to be sold; for example, the lion mark on a child's toy sold in Europe.

- Where necessary, products should include detailed instructions on use. When using an electric lawn mower or a food processor, for example, it would be essential to have detailed instructions.

- Where maintenance of a product may be carried out by consumers, it must be safe to do so; for example, when replacing the blade on an electric lawn mower or cleaning the blades on a food processor.

- Some products may need specific labelling about possible dangers; for example, a label on a light giving the safe maximum wattage of the light bulb.

You need to consider the working environment in which the products are manufactured and the conditions under which the workforce operates.

- The workplace must be well organised so that specific tasks may be carried out safely; for example, a heat treatment area such as a welding bay kept separate from other production areas.

- Walkways or gangways should be clearly marked and there should be specific areas where consumable goods or tools are stored out of the way to avoid obstacles.

- Chemicals, solvents, flammable and toxic substances must be stored and handled with extreme care. Employers are required by law to carry out 'risk assessments' of these substances. (Risk assessment is dealt with later in this chapter.)

- There should be adequate space at workstations so that the machine operators can work safely.

- Lighting should be adequate so that tasks can be carried out safely.

- The temperature in which employees work should be comfortable, taking into account the type of processes being undertaken.

- Where machinery is used, it is essential that:
  - instructions for use are clearly displayed near to the machine
  - warning hazards and regulations relating to safety clothing or eye protection are clearly displayed
  - companies provide adequate training in the use of machinery
  - emergency 'stop' buttons are provided
  - regular maintenance is carried out to ensure that tools are safe
  - faulty machinery should be clearly labelled and taken out of use.

- Procedures for emergency evacuation in the event of a fire and the reporting of accidents should be clearly displayed.

6.2 PERSONAL SAFETY

Personal protective wear

- Goggles provide eye protection when using the drilling machine, lathes, sanding disk or certain types of machine saw.

- Face masks or respirators should be used when spray painting and during any operation that creates dust, such as sanding, or toxic fumes.

- Visors give full face protection, for example, when casting hot metal.

- Aprons give general protection to clothing, while leather aprons are essential when casting hot metals.

- Leggings should be worn when casting hot metals.

- Steel-capped shoes should be worn where any heavy work is undertaken.

- Ear defenders should be used when drilling or cutting with heavy machinery.

- Rubber/plastic disposable gloves should be worn when using chemicals.

Some chemicals, such as catalysts and resins used in glass-fibre work, can harm the skin and may cause irritation, or even a skin disease called dermatitis. To minimise this risk, gloves should be worn. In addition, barrier cream rubbed into the hands and arms will provide a high level of protection. After use, the cream should be washed off with soap and water.

▌ Machine guards

Figure 6.1 Lathe guards

Machine guards are designed to protect you from a variety of dangers by enclosing the tool behind impact-resistant clear plastic shielding. Some guards, such as those around a drilling machine, are designed to adjust up and down as the drill bit is brought down onto the workpiece.

With some machines, the danger may be the sharpness of the cutting tool or an abrasive surface which can cause injury.

With many machines, the danger is the moving parts which could cause you or your clothing to become entangled in the machine.

Some of the machines you may be familiar with – such as drills, lathes and milling machines – must, by law, have adequate guards.

▌ Dust and fume extraction

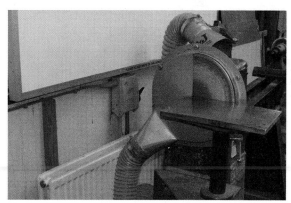

Figure 6.2 Dust extraction on a rotary sander

Precautions must be taken when carrying out processes that create dust, for example, using a sanding disk. Tiny particles of dust can be breathed in or enter your eyes.

Processes that create toxic fumes, such as spray painting or working with glass-reinforced plastic resins, also require great care.

Dust and fume extraction units are very effective when they are fitted closely and directly to the machine or equipment.

▶ Disposal of waste

Within most manufacturing environments, there is likely to be waste. It is important that waste materials are not allowed to build up and that they are disposed of properly. Much waste from wood, metal and plastic is relatively harmless, but chemicals need to be disposed of by specialist companies which collect them from the manufacturer's premises.

▶ Accident procedures

In the workshop it is essential that you know what to do in the event of an accident.

- Do not panic.
- Always tell your teacher immediately, no matter how minor you may consider the accident to be.
- Make sure you know where the first aid box is.
- Make sure you know where the emergency stop buttons are in the workshop.

▶ 6.3 RISK ASSESSMENT

Risk assessment is the process, required by law, to be undertaken by companies, including schools, to identify potentially dangerous situations in their workplace and to explain how the risks may be reduced or eliminated, so that everyone connected with the company or school can operate in a safe and healthy environment.

There are five stages in carrying out a risk assessment:

1. Identify the process, operation or substance.
2. Identify the possible hazard.
3. Consider the risk – that is, how likely it is that the hazard will occur.
4. Explain the control measures you need to carry out to provide protection.
5. Explain what emergency measures you need to carry out in the event of personal injury.

▶ 6.4 COSHH

COSHH stands for the Control of Substances Hazardous to Health. It is the way that employers assess the risks from using substances that could be very dangerous to our health; it is one part of risk assessment.

▶ Instructions relating to potentially hazardous substances

There are many potentially dangerous substances used in school workshops, including Tensol cement, superglue, impact adhesives and some paints. Your teachers will have carried out risk assessments for each of these substances.

Look at the following risk assessment for students and teachers using Tensol cement.

Process or operation	Hazards	Risk assessment	Control measures
Spreading cement onto surfaces of acrylic plastic to be joined together	May enter through the skin and by swallowing	There would have to be a huge spillage in the workshop or it would have to be used in a very confined space to pose a real hazard	Use in well-ventilated areas
	Irritant to the skin, eyes and lungs	Splashes from the cement would need to be kept off the skin and away from eyes	Apply barrier cream and/or wear protective gloves; eye protection must be worn
	Highly flammable	Vapour from Tensol could be ignited by flames or red-hot metal	Work must be kept at least 1 m away from flames or red-hot metal

Table 6.1 Risk assessment for Tensol cement

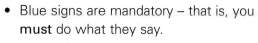

6.5 SAFETY SYMBOLS USED IN THE WORKSHOP

There will be a number of signs used in your workshop areas. You need to know what they mean and what you need to do to comply with them.

- Blue signs are mandatory – that is, you **must** do what they say.
- Black and yellow signs are warnings.
- Red diamonds are warnings of hazards.

Wash your hands

Wear eye protection

Wear ear protection

HIGHLY FLAMMABLE

Corrosive

Toxic

Chemicals

Figure 6.3 Safety signs

ACTIVITY

1. Make a room plan of one of your school workshops. Draw the positions of the workbenches, tables, cupboards, machines and emergency stop buttons. Make a list of all the 'good' or safe features and a list of all the 'poor' or potentially unsafe features.

2. Carry out two risk assessments when using:
    *   a drilling machine
    *   polyurethane varnish.

3. Look carefully at the student using the drilling machine in figure 6.4. Identify five safe working practices.

Figure 6.4

KEY TERMS

RISK ASSESSMENT is the process, required by law, to be undertaken by companies, including schools, to identify potentially dangerous situations in their workplace and to explain how the risks may be reduced or eliminated, so that everyone connected with the company or school can operate in a safe and healthy environment.

COSHH (Control of Substances Hazardous to Health) is the way that employers assess the risks from using substances that could be very dangerous to our health; it is one part of risk assessment.

CHAPTER 7

QUALITY

LEARNING OUTCOMES

**By the end of this chapter you should have developed
a knowledge and understanding of:**

- the difference between quality of design and manufacture
- factors that affect the quality of a product, such as the selection of materials and manufacturing processes
- dimensional accuracy in the component parts of an assembly
- 'tolerances' on working drawings
- simple quality control checks that can be carried out to ensure accuracy and quality of finish.

This chapter is all to do with quality. You will need to understand the difference between quality of design and quality of manufacture. When you undertake a practical project to make a single product, just as when a large manufacturing company starts mass production, you will need to put in place procedures to make sure that the manufactured products are of a consistently high quality. This is known as quality control. You will also need to have considered at the design stage what materials to use and the best methods of manufacture for those materials.

7.1 DISTINGUISHING BETWEEN QUALITY OF DESIGN AND QUALITY OF MANUFACTURE

It is very unlikely that manufacturing companies set out intentionally to make 'bad' products. It is not in their best interests, but it does happen. Sometimes a fault in a product may not occur until the product has been in use over a period of time. Very often, manufacturers have to 'recall' products because they have become potentially dangerous to the consumer. Sometimes the fault is caused by inappropriate materials, poor quality construction or assembly, or a fault in the basic design of the product.

▶ Why is 'quality' important to manufacturers?

- Manufacturers can actually save money by reducing waste and lost production time.
- Quality will make the company more efficient, by producing fewer faulty goods.
- Good-quality products enhance the reputation of the company, which can mean an increase in profit.

The Consumers' Association offers help and advice through their website and magazine, *Which?*. The monthly magazine gives details of tests carried out on a vast range of products. The products are tested against a list of criteria and given a percentage score. The best buys are clearly identified.

ACTIVITY

Go to the Which? website (www.which.co.uk) and find the most recent best buys for: digital cameras, mobile phones and hi-fi micro-systems.

When faults develop in products, the manufacturer or retailer often recalls the product so that the consumer can have the product repaired or replaced. Examples of two widely differing products recalled are the Nissan Qashqai motor car and the children's toy Sticklebricks.

Nissan Qashqai

Recall notices for Nissan Qashqai

Exact model: *Qashqai*

Description: *Potential loss of steering*

Build date: *25/6/07 to 30/06/07*

Numbers: *182*

Defect: *There is a possibility that a steering cover screw may not be sufficiently tight. This could lead initially to free play and noise in the steering which, if not attended to, could eventually result in the loss of steering control.*

Action: *Recall the vehicles that are likely to be affected to inspect and, where necessary, replace the steering gear.*

Sticklebricks

John Lewis Department Store

Product recall: *Sticklebricks*

John Lewis stock numbers: *789 42001 & 42002*

The manufacturer has identified a fault in some of the Sticklebricks produced since October 2007. The small 'stickles' can be detached and could be hazardous to young children. If you have purchased any since October 2007, please check, and if they are faulty, do not allow your child to continue playing with them and return them to us for a full refund.

Perhaps we should be relieved that when faults occur, manufacturers or retailers are quick to respond to the potential dangers and correct the situation.

The BBC television programme *Dragons' Den* provides 'inventors' seeking financial backing in order to develop and sell their products to a wide market with the opportunity to present their innovative products to a panel of business people. Very often the products are well made, but the panel decline to back the ideas because there are no commercial opportunities; the products are useless because they do not fulfil a need.

7.2 RELATIONSHIP BETWEEN MATERIAL AND MANUFACTURING PROCESS: CHOICE AND QUALITY

KEY POINT

- It is important that the right material is used to make a product as this can often have an effect on the quality of the finished item. The way the product is made can also affect quality, so the choice of processes and manufacturing methods to be used must also be carefully considered. It is always more expensive to make higher-quality products than more basic items, and a designer must consider what level of quality is actually needed in a product.

▶ Choice of material

With such a wide range of materials to choose from, a designer can take account of all the requirements of a product, including what level of quality is needed.

Items of furniture made from solid hardwoods such as oak and mahogany are of a high level of quality and are very expensive. To make the same items of furniture more cheaply, materials like pine and MDF can be used and covered with a thin veneer to give the appearance of being made from hardwood. Although the furniture may look similar to the more expensive, solid hardwood items, it is quite easy to tell that

the finished quality is lower by examining the grain of the wood and the plain edges of the MDF. If the finished quality is of no importance at all, simply using pine, plywood and MDF to make the furniture would be quite adequate, without the need for veneers or special finishes.

Figure 7.1 Quality furniture

Benches for use outside are often made from metal, to make them stronger and more durable. For cheapness, they can be made from steel, cast iron or aluminium and then coated to protect them from corrosion. When these coatings are damaged, however, the bare metal will quickly corrode and become unsightly and often dangerous. A bench made from stainless steel is expensive to produce but is of much higher quality and will remain so for many years, as it is strong and will not corrode.

In some cases, the choice of material for a product is restricted by the process used to

Figure 7.2 Stainless steel bench

make it. A good example of this is the use of brass for making water taps, because of the complex shapes that need to be produced. If the tap is to be used outside, it is normally left as bare brass because a high-quality appearance is not important. For use in bathrooms and kitchens, however, the taps are given a high-quality finish by chromium-plating the brass.

For many years it was felt that products made from plastics were always of poor quality, and the term 'plasticky' was often used to describe something that looked 'cheap and nasty'. Plastics materials have developed quickly over the years and so have the processes used to form them, so much so that it is now possible to give plastics the appearance of any other material. The advantage of this is that plastics can be formed easily into shapes that would be very difficult (and expensive) to produce in other materials, making quality products 'cheaply' without being 'cheap'.

Manufacturing processes

The choice of manufacturing process can often depend on the material that is being used and this may determine the overall quality of the product. Where a wider choice of processes is available, it should be remembered that some processes do produce higher-quality products than others. Generally speaking, it is more expensive to make higher-quality products, whether they are hand-made or produced in large quantities by machines.

In the case of the simple desk tidy shown in figure 7.4, there are a number of ways in which the product could be made; you may have made something quite similar as a project in your school workshop.

The desk tidy could be made in separate parts and then put together using a solvent

Figure 7.3 A quality plastic product

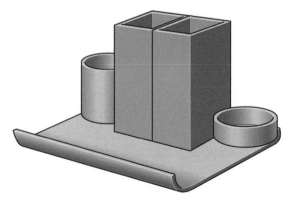

Figure 7.4 A simple desk tidy

adhesive such as polystyrene cement. If only one or a very small number were going to be made (one-off production) this would be a suitable way of making the product, but the joints between the parts would be visible. For larger numbers of desk tidies, the parts could be put together using a laser welding process, which would make the joints much neater and improve the appearance of the product. To mass-produce the desk tidy it would be made in one piece by injection-moulding, which would mean that there would be no joints to spoil the appearance of the product. By using the injection-moulding process it would also be easy to produce more complex shapes, to improve the functional quality of the desk tidy as well as its appearance.

ACTIVITY

1. Collect an assorted selection of basic products to evaluate and take a digital photograph of each one.

2. Suggest how you could improve the quality of each product by making it from a different material or by a different process (or both).

3. Give reasons for your choices of materials and processes in each case.

7.3 DIMENSIONAL ACCURACY

KEY POINT

- The accuracy that parts are made to is very important, particularly with the increase in volume production methods and the use of component parts made by other companies. Manufacturers need to be sure that all the parts required to make a product will fit together properly, and only accurate measurement of important dimensions can ensure this.

When we measure the size of something, we usually use a steel rule and occasionally a pair of outside or inside calipers. This method is quite satisfactory for normal measurement, but we can only really measure to the nearest

quarter of a millimetre. When a size is particularly important we need to be able to measure much more accurately than this to make sure parts fit together properly.

A number of tools are available for accurate measurement, including vernier calipers and

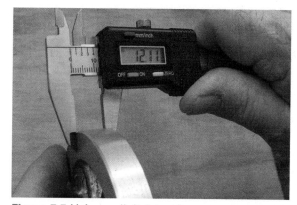

Figure 7.5 Using a digital vernier

micrometers, which can measure to an accuracy of 0.01 mm. Both of these tools are **precision** instruments and need to be used and handled carefully to maintain their accuracy.

Figure 7.6 Using a micrometer

Where the same dimension is to be checked many times, special **gauges** are used to allow the sizes to be checked more quickly and without mistakes. The main types of gauges are **gap** gauges for checking

thicknesses and **plug** gauges for checking the sizes of holes. In most cases, gauges are of a type referred to as **Go – No Go**, which means that the item being checked should fit the 'Go' part of the gauge but not the 'No Go' part. Some gauges come in standard forms and can be adjusted to a particular size, but others are specially made for checking one dimension only.

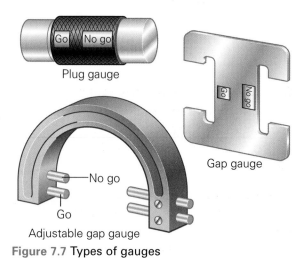

Figure 7.7 Types of gauges

7.4 TOLERANCE

KEY POINT

- When parts need to be assembled it is important that they fit together properly. While it would be possible to make every part to an exact size, this would take a very long time and would be very expensive. To make sure that parts can be made quickly and still fit together properly, important dimensions are given a **tolerance**, which is the amount by which a size is allowed to differ from the nominal size.

Figure 7.8 shows an axle shaft that is to fit into a hole in a wheel. The **nominal** size of the shaft and the hole is 25 mm. If the axle shaft is to be a 'sliding fit' in the wheel, the size of the hole in the wheel must always be slightly larger than the shaft. To make sure that this happens, a tolerance is put on the sizes of the hole and the axle shaft.

Hole in wheel – The hole must always be larger than the shaft, so if its nominal size is 25 mm, it can be allowed to be slightly more than this, but no less. The hole will therefore be given a tolerance of +0.02 / –0.00 mm.

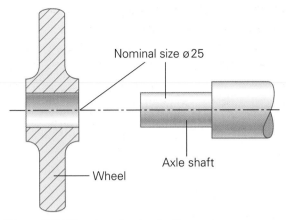

Figure 7.8 Wheel-and-axle shaft

The tolerance may be shown on the drawing by giving the actual allowable sizes, as shown in figure 7.9, rather than as + and − figures.

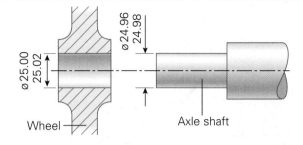

Figure 7.9 Dimensions of hole-and-axle shaft

Size of axle shaft – The size of the shaft must always be slightly less than the smallest allowable size of the hole. The 25 mm shaft will be given a tolerance of −0.02 / −0.04 mm.

This means that if the hole is the smallest allowable size and the shaft is the largest allowable size, there will be a clearance of 0.02 mm between them. With the largest hole and the smallest shaft, the clearance will be 0.06 mm. Any wheel that is made **within tolerance** will therefore have a clearance fit on any axle made within tolerance.

KEY TERMS

DIMENSION – The size of a particular part of an item shown on a drawing.
TOLERANCE – The allowable variation in an important dimension.
NOMINAL SIZE – A size given without any tolerance.

7.5 QUALITY CONTROL

When a product is manufactured, the company will set specific standards during the whole production process – that is, from the raw material to the finished product. **Quality control** is to do with monitoring these standards throughout production and involves two issues: inspection and testing.

Inspection

This involves examining the product and the materials used to make it at specific stages during the process, not just at the end. Inspection includes checks on:

- accuracy of sizes
- overall appearance
- surface finish

- the consistency, composition and structure of the materials.

When making a product in your school workshop you will have carried out quality control checks where you made similar inspections. For example, when clamping together the sides of a cabinet you will test it for squareness and check important sizes. When you give the cabinet its final coat of polyurethane varnish, you would check that there were no runs or brush strokes. You will look carefully all over the finished cabinet to check its overall appearance.

▶ Testing

Testing is to do with how well the product works. Testing is carried out to discover if the product works:

- as you intended it should
- in the specific location where it must operate
- over a period of time.

Depending on the type of product, some are tested to destruction, but most testing is non-destructive. When you carry out tests on a product you have made, you will refer to your design specification, which provides you with a 'shopping list' of specific issues you use to measure the success of your product.

EXAMINER'S TIPS

When examiners ask you to describe a quality control check on a product, try to be as specific as you can. For example, describe at *what stage* of manufacture the check would occur and *how* the check would be carried out – that is, using special tools and equipment or simply human eye. Do not confuse inspection with testing.

QUESTION

Imagine that you had made the toy train shown in figure 7.10. Describe two quality control checks that you would have carried out during its manufacture and two tests you would carry out to find how good the toy train is in use. Also write some specification points for the train.

Figure 7.10

KEY TERM

QUALITY CONTROL – When a product is manufactured, the company will set specific standards during the whole production process – that is, from the raw material to the finished product. Quality control is to do with monitoring these standards throughout production and involves two issues: inspection and testing.

CHAPTER 8

UNIT A561: INTRODUCTION TO DESIGNING AND MAKING

LEARNING OUTCOMES

By the end of this chapter you should have developed a knowledge and understanding of:

- Analysing an existing product
- Responding to a design brief
- Producing a design specification
- Generating and communicating design ideas
- Producing and communicating a final design proposal
- Planning the making of a product
- Making a prototype product
- Solving technical problems
- Recording the stages of making a product
- Evaluating the processes involved in designing and making a prototype product.

This unit of work will involve you in researching, designing, modelling and making a prototype product and then evaluating your work. If you are taking the full GCSE qualification, this work will be 30 per cent of your total marks. If you are taking the GCSE short course, the work will be 60 per cent of your total marks. In both cases this work will take 20 hours.

In this piece of work you will have to select a product or group of similar products to study as a starting point for your designing and making. The photographs shown in figures 8.1–8.10 are typical starting points. The available starting points allowed by the examination board may change slightly from year to year. It is important to check that you are using the correct starting points. Your teacher will give you a list of these for the examination session in which you are entered.

Typical starting points for unit A561

Figure 8.1 Celebrations – a collection of trophies

Figure 8.2 Travel – a travel game

Figure 8.3 Sustainability – a product using reduce, reuse or recycle as a starting point

Figure 8.4 Blast from the past – a stand for a recipe book

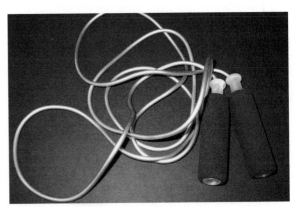

Figure 8.5 Sport – a skipping rope; this could be designed to include a method of lengthening or shortening the rope

Figure 8.6 Lighting – a collection of commercially available lighting units

Figure 8.7 Educational toys – a toy that helps children learn a skill as well as providing entertainment and enjoyment

Figure 8.10 Storage – a box used to store and organise a large collection of photographs

You will then go on to **either**:

- design and make a prototype product, to improve the product you have studied in some way

or:

- design and make a prototype for a similarly functioning product of your own.

In both cases you will have to produce a well-crafted prototype product and then evaluate the processes involved in designing and making it.

Figure 8.8 The great outdoors – a small camping stool

▶ Important guidelines and procedures

You should make your own judgements and decisions, and take responsibility for the direction in which your project moves. Your teacher will advise, support and assist you by suggesting approaches, alternatives and possibilities, and by directing you to appropriate resources.

Figure 8.9 Display – a collection of stamped pennies from around the world

Throughout the project you must remember that you will have to sign a declaration saying that the work is your own original work. Where some of the work is carried out outside the centre, it is important that your teacher is able to confirm that the work is your own. Sufficient work must be carried out under the direct supervision of your teacher for the whole of your work to be verified.

If you are working with other students on a group project, you must identify and take responsibility for uniquely definable aspects of the overall product. Ultimately, your work must constitute a complete project in its own right and provide evidence for assessment against each of the assessment criteria.

It is important that you acknowledge clearly the source of all information and assistance at the appropriate point in your record of designing and making. This includes extracts from newspapers, magazines, catalogues, websites, CD-ROMs, photocopied materials and practical assistance with making tasks.

Assessment and submission of controlled assessment work

The project is not just about assessment and helping you to gain a qualification; it is also about you enjoying your work and 'learning by doing'.

You should structure your work to follow the assessment criteria, and present your work in section number order. Your work can be submitted on paper or in electronic format, but not a mixture of both.

Work submitted on paper

A contents page with a numbering system should be included to aid organisation. All your work should be on the same size paper, but it does not matter what size paper you choose. You can produce your work by hand

or using ICT, but you should remember that it is the content of the work which is important and no extra marks will be gained just by word-processing your work, for example.

Work submitted electronically

Your work will need to be organised in folders so that the evidence can be accessed easily by a teacher or moderator. This structure is commonly known as a folder tree. There should be a top-level folder detailing your centre number, candidate number, surname and forename, together with the unit code A561. The next folder down should be called 'Home Page', which will be an index of all your work. The evidence for each section of the work should then be stored in a separate folder, containing appropriately named files. These files can be from the Microsoft® Office suite, movie, audio, graphics, animation, structured markup or text formats. Microsoft PowerPoint® is an ideal platform for producing electronic portfolios.

The importance of the right project choice

You will have to select a product or group of similar products as a starting point for your designing and making. Your teacher will give you a product or a list of possible products as a starting point for all projects in your teaching group. When you select your product, you must remember you will not be allowed to study the same theme in Unit A563.

Your school may also set a common design brief based on the product you have studied as a starting point for all projects in your teaching group, or you may be asked to write a design brief of your own.

The purpose of this project is to show your abilities in designing, making and evaluating. If you are to write your own design brief, your project will need to:

- be challenging, to allow you to achieve the grade you are capable of, but not so difficult that you are unable to complete the work
- display creativity and innovation
- result in a complete high-quality prototype product
- be realistic and manageable within the time and resources available, including the expertise of your teachers.

Remember:

- you need to be realistic when writing your design brief and listen to the advice of your teachers
- the size of your project is not important – small, carefully designed and made prototype products will often outscore larger prototype products
- cost of materials and pre-manufactured components can be a problem.

Characteristics of a successful project

- Good planning and organisation
- Clear focus on what your target user group would like
- Creativity and refinement
- High-quality work and attention to detail
- Understanding the impact your product may have on the environment
- Good use of computer-aided design in generating a design proposal and, if appropriate, good use of computer-aided

manufacture in making components for your prototype product
- Clear and careful communication and presentation

Section by section

A maximum of 60 marks are available for this work. The 60 marks will be divided into six sections, as shown in Table 8.1.

Section	Marks
Analysis of existing product(s)	10
Designing	14
Planning and making your prototype product safely	20
Solving technical problems	4
Recording the making of your prototype product	4
Evaluation of the processes involved in designing, modelling and making the prototype product	8

Table 8.1 Sections and marks for Unit A561

KEY POINT

- You will need to think about how you use the time you have available, making sure that you spend longer on the sections that can be awarded more marks and less time on those sections with fewer marks.

You will need to hand the following items to your teacher when you have completed the work.

Design worksheets

These will be in either electronic or paper form. They will contain all the design and evaluation work you have done.

A prototype product

This will be your final prototype product.

Digital images/photographs

These will be included as part of the design worksheets above and will include:

- a view of the front of your prototype product
- a view of the back of your prototype product
- views of any models or mock-ups you made when designing and modelling.

A cover sheet

This will be the completed OCR examination board cover sheet, which will include details of your name, school, candidate number and so on.

▶ Section 1 Analysis of existing product(s)

Analyse an existing product or group of similar products to:

- consider how well the product(s) meet the needs of the user
- identify significant trends in existing solutions.

Look carefully at the products you have identified and start by recording factual information about them; this will include:

- cost
- size
- weight
- the materials that have been used
- the methods of construction that have been used
- the finish that has been applied to the product

Assessment criteria	Marks
• Identify complex associations linking principles of good design and technological knowledge, relating products to user's needs and wants • Demonstrate and understand the significance of trends in existing solutions; reinterpret and apply this understanding in imaginative ways	8–10
• Identify associations linking principles of good design and the technological knowledge, relating products to user's needs • Demonstrate the significance of research that identifies trends in existing solutions; interpret and apply this understanding in a design context	4–7
• Make simple/limited links between principles of good design and technological knowledge, showing limited awareness of the user • Identify one or two trends in existing solutions and use this understanding in a design context	0–3

Table 8.2 Assessment criteria and marks for Section 1

- features the product has that enable it to do the job for which it was designed
- features that are common to some of the existing products you are looking at
- safety features.

You also need to think about how the product you are studying has changed over the years and how it may change in the future. Why have these changes taken place?

Having looked at the existing products as described above, think about if there are any aspects of the product that could be further improved, considering what the user would like the product to do. Record your thoughts carefully. You will use this analysis as a starting point for your designing and making as you progress through this project.

Figure 8.13 Analysing a chess table

Figure 8.11 Analysing an aluminium CD holder

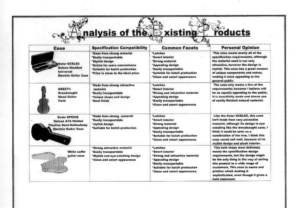

Figure 8.12 Analysing guitar cases

Section 2 Designing

- Respond to a design brief and produce a specification for a prototype product.
- Create design ideas and communicate them using a range of appropriate techniques.
- Produce detailed and annotated drawings to communicate all the details of your chosen design proposal.

Responding to a design brief

A good way to start this section is to use the five Ws method outlined in chapter 1 (page 5). You will need to communicate with the user group for your product to find out exactly what they require. To do this, you can conduct a questionnaire, survey or interview and then write a conclusion about what you have found.

Other useful activities in responding to your design brief are:

- considering what social, moral, cultural and environmental issues are relevant to the product
- collecting relevant measurable information on anthropometrics, sizes, weights, capacities, quantities and costs

- collecting relevant information on safety or other consumer legislation
- collecting relevant information about pre-manufactured components, materials, constructional methods and finishes.

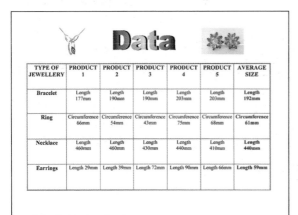

Figure 8.14 Collecting sizes of jewellery in preparation for designing a jewellery container

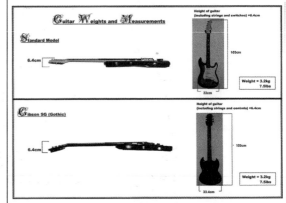

Figure 8.15 Collecting sizes and weights of guitars in preparation for designing a guitar case

Assessment criteria	Marks
• Demonstrate an appropriate and considered response to a brief and produce a detailed specification for a prototype as a result of analysis • Produce creative and original ideas by generating, developing and communicating design using appropriate strategies • Use drawing and annotation clearly to communicate details of the design chosen for prototype production	11–14
• Demonstrate an appropriate response to a brief and produce a suitable specification for a prototype product as a result of analysis • Produce creative ideas and communicate these by using appropriate strategies • Use drawing and annotation to communicate most details of the design chosen for prototype production	5–10
• Demonstrate a limited response to a brief and produce a simple specification for a prototype product • Produce one or two simple design ideas using a limited range of strategies • Use drawing and annotation to communicate limited and incomplete details of the design chosen for prototype production	0–4

Table 8.3 Assessment criteria and marks for Section 2

Producing a specification

The design specification is a list of the design requirements for the product you are designing. Detailed information about specifications can be found in chapter 1 (page 10). The specification will be a conclusion to all the work you have done on the project so far. It will give you a focus for producing design ideas.

Look carefully at the information you have gathered. What are the key requirements for your product? List these requirements as bullet points and make sure that your specification includes all of the following:

- performance criteria – precisely what the product has to do; properties of materials and finishes that are important; expected lifespan
- measurable details – maximum or minimum sizes, weights, capacities, quantities and costs
- aesthetics – colour, proportion and texture
- manufacturing – scale of production and economics

- user factors – ergonomics, safety, legislation, handling, storage and maintenance
- environmental aspects – the product in use and disposal.

Producing creative ideas

When you start designing, you need to think of as many ideas as you can and record them with simple drawings that you can look at again later. The more ideas you put down, the better, as the more ideas you have, the more likely it is that one of your ideas is a really good one. Just put down ideas quickly, think as widely as you can and do not worry if your ideas seem a bit crazy at first.

You should annotate your ideas to:

- communicate features of an idea which you think are particularly promising
- highlight features of the idea that could be a problem and require further thought
- show overall sizes
- show ideas for materials that could be used
- show ideas for methods of construction that could be used
- show ideas for finishes that could be used.

Remember that there are marks for communicating your designs using a range of different methods. Some of the techniques you may wish to use include:

- simple 2D and 3D pencil sketches
- 3D drawings using coloured pencils or marker pens for shading
- computer-generated 2D modelling
- 3D models using card or other modelling materials to develop your ideas further.

DESIGN SPECIFICATION

1] It must have at least 560mm of leg room.
When playing a game at a table people will want to be able to sit down comfortably without their legs being cramped. To ensure this the table must have at least 560mm of leg room to allow enough room for their legs.

2] It must have an integrated chessboard in the tabletop.
An integrated chessboard on top of the table will make the product appear more interesting and aesthetically pleasing for people, and also enhance it practical function. Even if the customers are not regular chess players, a sale is more likely because of that extra touch of class.

3] It must cost less than £50 in raw materials.
The manufacture cost is of great significance. If the cost of manufacture is too high, the profit will be less or the number of sales will be less because of the extortionate price. I feel that the table must cost less than £50 to ensure a quality product that will not cost more than the customer is prepared to pay. Also, I have a budget which I must keep to.

4] It must use jigs and templates to ensure a quality product.
Jigs and templates are of great importance especially if more than one of my product is going to be made. Jigs will aid in batch production and ensure consistency. By use of aids, the products will be the same size and all of the joints will be of the highest quality.

5] The finish must be able to withstand scratches and liquids.
Usually when playing board games, people will want to be able to have a drink without worrying about scratching or damaging the surface of the table if they spill a drink upon it. This means that the product must have a good finish, which will protect the wood from scratches and small spills, such as a polyurethane varnish.

6] It must be possible to make several objects at one time by batch production.
In order to make my product by batch production the use of jigs and templates will be needed to ensure all the products will be the same size and quality. I will only be making one product but it must be possible to make more than one of the product at one time if the need should arise.

7] It must be aesthetically pleasing.
Customers will want an aesthetically pleasing product so it is very important to provide one. This means all the joints must fit perfectly and good quality wood must be used to achieve a high quality appearance. The right finish which will bring out the best in the wood must be used as well. For instance, if oak is used, a varnish must be used to bring out the grain.

8] It must be strong and stable.
The table must be of good strength and stable. This means that if it were to be accidently knocked, it would not fall over nor would any joints break or become loose.

9] It must retail at less than £150.
To be of a competitive price the table must retail at less than £150. If the price is too high, there would be no customers willing to buy the product, if the price is too low the profit will not be great enough to support the cost of labour and materials.

10] The table top must have a width between 450mm and 550mm.
To be able to play a board game the table must be wide enough. With a width between 450mm and 550mm, this will ensure there is enough room for board games and the table will be of a size whereupon it can still be easily manufactured, stored and transported.

11] It must take less than 30 hours to make.
The manufacture time must be kept low because otherwise the labour cost will be too high and the product will have to overpriced to account for this. I only have a limited amount of hours available in the workshop for construction.

12] It must have room for storage.
It is very important as shown in my questionnaire, storage space is listed very highly in the user's requirements. It must be able to hold cards and chess pieces.

Figure 8.16 A specification for a chess table

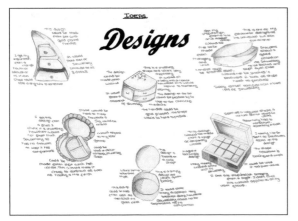
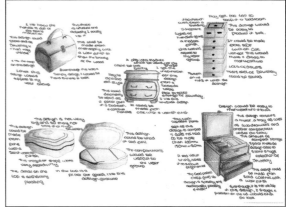

Figure 8.17 Some design ideas for a jewellery container

Communicating the details of your final design

KEY POINT

- When you start this section you should remember that you are making a prototype product.

Because you are making a prototype, it may well be that the prototype product is not made:

- from the same materials as a real product
- using the same methods of construction that would be used for a real product
- using the same finish that would be used for a real product.

For example, you may design a product that would be made using injection-moulded plastic as a real product, but the prototype you make for this piece of work could be made from small pieces of timber joined together and sprayed to represent the real product you are designing.

You will need to show all the information that is required to enable your product to be made. A combination of drawings and notes will be needed. The usual method for drawing a final design is orthographic projection, but you can use any method of drawing as long as your drawings and notes show:

- the shape of each component to be made
- the size of each component to be made
- the materials to be used for each component
- details of the finish to be used on each component
- details of any pre-manufactured components
- details of the methods and processes used to assemble the product.

Section 3 Planning and making your prototype product safely

- Select materials, tools and equipment to make your prototype product.
- Produce a step-by-step plan to make your prototype product.
- Work skilfully and safely to produce a quality prototype product.

Assessment criteria	Marks

• Plan and organise activities:
  – select and use appropriate materials
  – select and use hand and machine tools as appropriate to realise the product
• Work skilfully and safely to assemble, construct and finish materials and components as appropriate to achieve a quality prototype product
• Assess and apply knowledge of the workshop/design studio facilities as appropriate to realise the prototype product
	14–20

• Plan and organise activities:
  – select and use appropriate materials
  – select and use hand and machine tools as appropriate to realise the product
• Work effectively and safely to assemble, construct and finish materials and components as appropriate to achieve a good quality prototype product
• Choose and use workshop/design studio facilities as appropriate to realise the prototype product
	7–13

• Plan and organise activities:
  – select and use appropriate materials
  – select and use hand and machine tools as appropriate to realise the product
• Work safely to assemble, construct and finish materials and components as appropriate to generate a prototype product
• Use workshop/design studio facilities as appropriate to realise the prototype product
	0–6

Table 8.4 Assessment criteria and marks for Section 3

You need to plan very carefully how you are going to make your prototype product. This will involve writing a step-by-step plan for making each component, including:

• the tools and equipment to be used

• details of any safety precautions that need to be taken at each stage

• an estimate of how long each stage will take; this can be set out in a table, as shown in Figure 1.43 (page 22).

You will also need to plan the quality assurance methods you will require and at what stages quality control will be necessary.

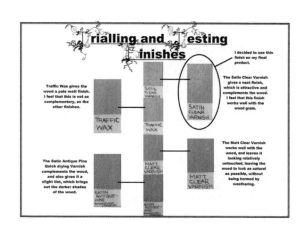

Figure 8.18 Selecting finishes

You will see from the assessment criteria in table 8.4 that to gain high marks you will need to:

- select materials, tools and equipment carefully
- work skilfully to make your prototype product, using the facilities in your centre's workshops and design studios.

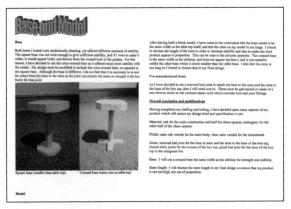

Figure 8.19 Using modelling to make some final design decisions

Assessment criteria	Marks
• Demonstrate a practical and thorough understanding and ability in solving technical problems effectively and efficiently as they arise	4
• Demonstrate a practical understanding and ability in solving some technical problems as they arise	2–3
• Demonstrate a simple understanding of how to solve a technical problem as it arises	0–1

Table 8.5 Assessment criteria and marks for Section 4

▶ Section 4 Solving technical problems

Demonstrate how you have solved technical problems as they have arisen.

Technical problems are likely to arise in two different ways:

- technical problems that have been foreseen before the prototype product is made
- technical problems that have only come to light during the manufacture of the prototype product.

You should therefore record:

- how you solved any technical problems as the product was developed from an initial idea to a final design proposal for production
- any changes that have been made to your final design proposal as the product is being made.

You should not be concerned if you need to make changes to your final design, as things do not always go entirely to plan, even for the most experienced designers. It is far more important to solve problems if they arise rather than ignoring them.

▶ Section 5 Recording the making of your prototype product

Record the key stages in making your prototype product, using notes and photographic evidence.

You need to keep a record or log of all the stages of making your product. This will include some or all of the following:

- marking out materials
- cutting out each component

- marking out holes and/or joints
- cutting out holes and/or joints
- details of quality assurance or quality control checks used
- details of finishing techniques and applied finishes used
- details of each stage of the product's assembly.

You will need to use notes and sketches and take photographs of the operations listed above as they are carried out. If you are going to present your work in electronic format, you can also use short sections of video to show operations such as a laser cutter producing a component.

Assessment criteria	Marks
• Record key stages involved in the making of the prototype product; provide comprehensive notes and photographic evidence	4
• Record key stages involved in the making of the prototype product; provide notes and photographic evidence	2–3
• Simply record the making of the prototype product, using notes and/or photographic evidence	0–1

Table 8.6 Assessment criteria and marks for Section 5

Stages of manufacturing

Drilling- we had to drill a lot of holes to join it all together we also used different sizes of hole for things like the shelf. We had to drill a lot of holes to attach the wood together to make it strong and flat packable.

Hole cutting-

We had to cut holes in the backboard to make room for plugs and cables to come through. This process was quick and easy. The hardest thing to do was to get it in the centre

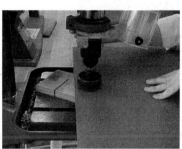

Counter boring- we did counter drilling to make it look neat and to make the joints tight so that the K.D. bolts will fit in well

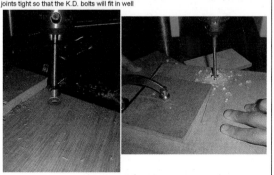

Marking out

We had to do a lot of marking out; this is a hard process and if you get the marking wrong the whole thing will not go together and then you had to mark out the whole piece of wood again

Figure 8.20 Recording the stages in making a CD and DVD rack

Plane

We had to plane the wood to make a lip for the back board to sit on. We do this to make it look neat and fit in tight to the piece of wood.

Plug cutting

We cut out plugs to put over the holes that we have drilled to make the cabinet neater this makes it look very neat.

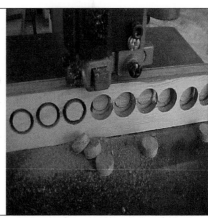

Assembling

We had to attach lots of bits of wood together using lots of different methods like gluing and using K.D. joints. There were so many bits of wood to attach it took a long time.

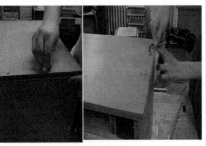

Figure 8.20 continued

> ## Section 6 Evaluation of the processes involved in designing, modelling and making the prototype product

- Evaluate the processes involved in designing and making the prototype product.
- Produce proposals for modifications to improve the modelling and prototyping process.

You need to think about how successful the designing of the product was and comment on the following:

- Did you spend too much time on some

KEY POINT

- This section of your assignment is about evaluating the **processes** involved in designing and making your prototype product. It is not about evaluating the prototype product itself.

aspect of the work and not enough on others?
- Did you write a specification that was sufficiently detailed and did the specification provide a good basis from which to evaluate your ideas?
- Did you select the most appropriate materials for making the prototype product?
- Did you select the most appropriate method of construction for the prototype product?
- Did you select the most appropriate finish for the prototype product?

Assessment criteria	Marks
• Critically evaluate the process involved in designing and making the prototype • Reflect and suggest modifications to improve the modelling and prototype process • Specialist terms will be used appropriately and correctly • The information will be presented in a structured format • The candidate can demonstrate the accurate use of spelling, punctuation and grammar	6–8
• Give an evaluation of the making process • Reflect on how to improve the modelling and prototyping process • There will be some use of specialist terms, although these may not always be used appropriately • The information given will be presented for the most part in a structured format • There may be occasional errors in spelling, punctuation and grammar	3–5
• Give limited evaluation of the modelling and prototyping process • There will be little or no use of specialist terms • Answers may be ambiguous and disorganised • Errors in spelling, punctuation and grammar may be intrusive	0–2

Table 8.7 Assessment criteria and marks for Section 6

CHAPTER 9

UNIT A562: SUSTAINABLE DESIGN

LEARNING OUTCOMES

By the end of this chapter you should have developed knowledge and understanding of:

- the 6Rs
- social issues
- moral issues
- cultural issues
- environmental issues
- design issues.

This unit of the GCSE course aims to develop your knowledge and understanding of sustainability, environmental concerns, cultural, moral and social issues.

Industrial Technology
Resistant Materials
Textiles Technology
Design Technology
Graphics
Electronics and Control Systems
Food Technology

Figure 9.1 Design Technology subject areas

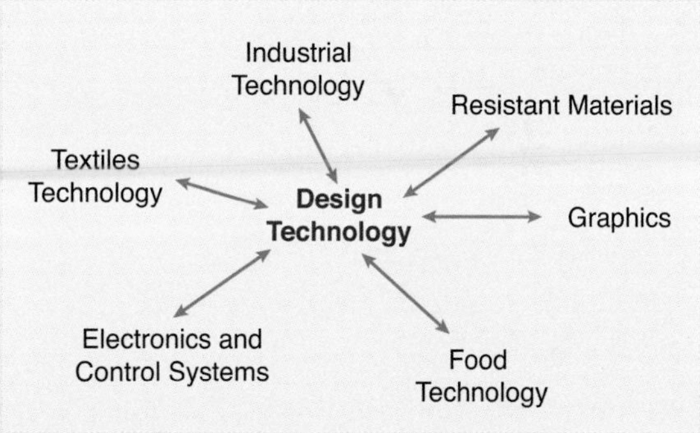

You will look at how design and technology has evolved through analysis of products from the past and the present within your specialist subject area. You will need to consider how future designs/products will impact on the world in which we live.

By looking at old and new products, you will gain awareness and understanding of trends, and innovations in design, manufacture, labelling and packaging, and the impact that the design of such products is having on the environment, society and the economy.

10.1 OVERVIEW OF THE UNIT

Moral, cultural, economic, environmental and sustainability issues are an important part of design and technology. Through this unit you will be able to answer some of the following questions:

- What is meant by a 'product life cycle'?
- Why were certain materials chosen and used?
- What is meant by planned obsolescence?
- What do we mean by the six Rs?
- What can we do to ensure that the eventual disposal of products/materials is as eco-friendly as possible?

The assessment of this unit is through an externally set and marked test.

- You will answer this using your knowledge of your specialist subject/material area.
- This unit can be taken in either the January or the June examination session.
- The unit can be retaken once, with the best result used.
- It represents 20 per cent of a full GCSE qualification or 40 per cent of a short course qualification.
- The maximum mark for the unit is 60.
- The duration of the examination is one hour and the paper is divided into two sections.
- **Section A** will consist of 15 short-answer questions. They will be a mixture of multiple choice, one-word answers and true or false questions. The section will carry 15 marks in total. It is expected that you will spend 15 minutes on this section.

Examplar question:
Which of the following is **not** a renewable energy resource?

(a) water
(b) coal
(c) wind
(d) solar panel

- **Section B** consists of 3 questions which will require you to relate your knowledge and understanding of the six Rs, materials, processes and the design of products.

Each question will be marked out of 15 marks. The questions may involve sketching, annotation, short sentences or more extended writing. It is expected that you will spend 45 minutes of this section.

Exemplar question:
(a) Identify a product that could be recycled
(b) Explain why you have chosen this product and how it can be recycled [2]

In Section B, your quality of written 'communication' will be assessed as well as your knowledge and understanding. Questions where this is to be done will be marked with an asterisk (*) and will usually ask you to discuss or explain something in detail.

Exemplar question:
* Products become 'obsolete' after a few years. Discuss the difference between fashion and planned obsolescence. [6]

Make sure you understand the 'command' words that are used in examination papers.

'State...name...give'

This requires a specific name of, for example, a piece of equipment, material or process

'Complete'

This requires you to complete, for example, a table, design or drawing.

'Describe'

This requires you to give an idea of, for example, how something works or what is involved in a process.

'Use sketches and notes to...'

You can use either or both here and it is important that the notes support and expand upon the sketches used.

'Explain'

This requires a detailed account of something including reasons, justifications or comparisons. This type of question will carry two or more marks.

'Discuss'

When you are asked to 'discuss' you must give well-reasoned points and explanations, adding examples to show the examiner what you are thinking. One-word answers, lists or bullet points are not acceptable for this type of question.

The 6Rs

RETHINK	How can it do the job better? Is it energy efficient? Has it been designed for disassembly?
REUSE	Which parts can I use again? Has it another valuable use without processing it?
RECYCLE	How easy is it to take apart? How can the parts be used again? How much energy is used to reprocess parts?
REPAIR	Which parts can be replaced? Which parts are going to fail? How easy is it to replace parts?
REDUCE	Which parts are not needed? Do we need as much material? Can we simplify the product?
REFUSE	Is it really necessary? Is it going to last? Is it fair trade? Is it unfashionable to be trendy and too costly to be stylish?

Figure 9.2 The 6Rs

EXAMINER'S TIPS

Key skills to achieve high marks in this unit are as follows:

- Think about design with an open mind, and be aware of changes that are happening.
- Recall, select, use and communicate knowledge and understanding of concepts, issues and terminology within your material area.
- Record ideas showing design thinking, innovation and flair; this will involve detailed notes and, where appropriate, high-quality sketches and annotated drawings.
- Seek out and use information from existing designers.
- Analyse and evaluate design and production skills and techniques.
- Understand materials and components in the context of the chosen product.
- Consider how past and present design technology affects society.
- Demonstrate understanding of the wider effects of design and technology on issues including sustainability, society, the economy and the environment.

Figure 9.3 Recycling logo

Figure 9.4 Clothing rail

Recycle

Recycling is what we do with the objects we use in our daily lives. Recycling is the conversion of waste products into new materials, to extend the life and usefulness of a product, item or object that seems to have no more purpose or use once it has been finished with or used for its initial purpose. Recycling means reusing a product; but sometimes, before a product can be reused, it will need to undergo processing or treatment.

The three main types of recycling are:

- primary recycling
- secondary or physical recycling
- tertiary or chemical recycling.

Primary recycling

The second-hand use of items – whether clothing-, electronic- or product-based – is a form of primary recycling as the item is simply being used again. Charity shops stock a large selection of recycled products. Giving items to friends and relatives or selling them on internet market sites are all ways of primary recycling.

Secondary or physical recycling

This is the process in which waste materials are recycled into different types of products. The change the product will go through depends on the main fibre or material of the product. Some products can be left to biodegrade before being regenerated into something else. Packaging used for food is often difficult to recycle. However, biodegradable packaging such as 'potatopak' has been developed.

ACTIVITY

Carry out some research into biodegradable packaging and look at the advantages and disadvantages of this type of packaging. List the materials the packaging is made from and research alternative materials that it would be possible to recycle.

Tertiary or chemical recycling

Products are broken down and reformulated – for example, plastic bottles can be recycled into fibres and then respun into polyester to make fleece fabric used for coats and blankets. Car tyres can be reused to make numerous products, such as computer mouse mats.

Figure 9.5 Old tyres

Recyclable materials include glass, paper, metals, wood, textiles, electronics, tyres, plastics and food wastes. Most, if not all, things can be recycled in some way.

rapidly filling up rubbish dumps all over the world; as this happens our concerns for the environment grow. When designing and making a new product, designers and manufacturers need to consider how their product can be recycled at the end of its lifespan.

You will need to know about the following:

- materials that can be recycled
- products that use recycled materials
- disassembly – reprocessing materials for use in new products.

QUESTIONS

1. What does the term recycling mean?
2. List three products that can be recycled.
3. Name a material made from recycled products.

Figure 9.6 Paper being recycled at a waste collection plant

Figure 9.7 Recycling – plastic, metal, glass and paper

Why recycle?

Everything we dispose of goes somewhere, although once the container or bag of rubbish is out of our hands and out of our houses we forget it instantly. Our consumer lifestyle is

Reuse

Products that can be reused for either the same purpose or a new purpose
Products that are designed to be reused result in less waste, which leads to

conservation of materials and resources. Many places around the UK collect unwanted products or repair them for redistribution for the same or a similar end use.

Products that can be adapted to suit an alternative use

Some local areas have set up their own websites and organisations for the reuse of unwanted items, involving groups of people who actively aim to adapt existing products for alternative uses.

Reduce

Life cycle of a product

A new product progresses through a variety of stages, from the original idea to its decline where it might be discontinued or disposed of. You must consider the impact of a product on the environment and its impact on society as a whole. The main stages involved are as follows:

- The raw materials – how are they harvested/made?

- The production process – how is the product made?

- Transport and distribution – what, how, where and how much does it cost?

- Uses – what are the intended uses of the product? How will they be used by the client or the customer?

- Recycling – how can the product be recycled?

- Care and maintenance – what is needed, how much is needed and is it environmentally friendly?

- Disposal – the waste from manufacturing or the product itself. Is it recyclable or biodegradable?

KEY TERM

LIFE CYCLE – The stages a new product goes through, from conception to eventual decomposition.

Eco footprint

This is the term used to refer to the measurement of our actions on the environment. As a designer, you must consider the effect of your product on the environment, from the first stages of your design ideas to the final making and eventual disposal or recycling of your product. Your footprint involves showing that you have designed the product with the environment in mind and have tried to minimise the damage caused by the various stages throughout your product's life cycle.

Built-in obsolescence

This is where the product has been designed to last for a set period of time. The functions of the product have been designed by the manufacturer to fail after a certain time limit. The consumer is then under pressure to purchase again. This built-in obsolescence is in many different products, from vehicles to light bulbs, from items of clothing to food 'use by' or 'best before' dates. Manufacturers can invest money to make the product obsolete more quickly, by making the product with cheaper components, which speeds up this planned obsolescence.

Energy and waste of production process

The consumption of non-renewable energy resources such as coal and oil is causing an energy crisis. These resources will eventually run out. Using non-renewable resources adds to the pollution problem, as products made from oil often take a long time to break down in the environment. Transportation of products is a high user of oil and petrol – refined fossil fuels. 'Green energy' is the leader of alternative energy sources which are considered environmentally friendly and non-polluting. Energy is generated from the following natural sources:

- wind
- solar
- geothermal
- hydro
- tidal/wave.

Figure 9.8 Wind turbines

EXAMINER'S TIPS

The following questions are open-ended questions and will require your answer to discuss relevant points in the context of your subject/material area.

Use of specialist terms and appropriate use of factual information will allow you to score at the higher mark level.

QUESTIONS

1. Do methods of transportation harm the environment?
2. Are we using too much electricity or too many chemicals that could harm our environment?
3. What alternative sources of energy are available?

Materials – waste

We often overlook how much we waste as consumers, whether it be consumable products, power sources such as electricity, or packaging. Waste management is a growing problem, from chemicals that get into the water system, to paper and card used in packaging. Switching off our computers or not leaving the television on standby can help us to reduce the energy we waste. Reusing carrier bags or buying locally made products helps to reduce material waste and bring about a more eco-friendly footprint. Manufacturers now have to follow guidelines on how to get rid of their waste effluent. Research into effective management of pollution, energy and other material waste is ongoing. You need to be aware of current changes within these areas.

Refuse

Issues relating to sustainable design

Processing, manufacturing, packaging and transportation of our products use huge amounts of energy and can create lots of waste. You need to look at the sustainability of a product from an environmental and social viewpoint. How is the product made and can we ensure that no or little harm is introduced into the environment by this method of manufacture? Sometimes a choice between the performance of the product required and the impact on the environment by its manufacture has to be considered and debated.

Materials we should refuse to use

Why should you refuse to use some products? The answer includes a variety of reasons, as set out below:

- The product may be made unnecessarily from man-made instead of natural sources.
- Toxic chemicals may be used in the product.
- What about the manufacturing process itself? Has the product been made in compliance with safety regulations?
- What about the rights of the workers and the conditions they have been working in?
- What packaging has been used and what are the transport distances and costs?
- It might not be good for you – for example, high fat content.

You should think about these issues before you accept a product and, above all, do not buy it if you do not need it!

Rethink

Consider your lifestyle and that of others close to you, and think about how you buy products and the energy required to use them. Society is constantly evolving and changing and you can evaluate how you could make a difference.

- How it is possible to approach design problems differently? What ideas can you develop to ensure a difference?
- What could you design using an existing product that has become waste, to use the materials or components for another purpose, without processing the product?

ACTIVITY

1. In groups, discuss what makes you want to buy a product.
2. Discuss and consider what you have bought recently and why. Did you really need it?

Repair

Today's throwaway society means it is quicker and easier to throw something away than to repair it. We looked at built-in obsolescence earlier in this chapter, where manufacturers encourage consumers to repurchase rather than repair.

- Some products you can repair yourself; others have to be taken to repair shops.
- Some products are beyond repair or would cost too much to fix.
- Unwanted electronic and electrical equipment is the fastest-growing waste area. Why? The need to change attitudes in this area is enormous. How can this be achieved?

Social issues

Today we live in a global society. You need to be aware of the ways this can affect the designing of products. Products need to be designed for use by a range of different cultures and nationalities, all of which may have different specific needs. Society has become multicultural and diverse; some products may be designed for a specific section of society, while others may be universal.

Figure 9.9 Logo depicting global unity

Social issues include:

- social development: through recognising the need to consider the views of others when designing and discussing designed products

- understanding the relationship between man and the general environment

- economic development cycle of a range of products and the impact on individuals, societies and countries

- issues associated with economic development and employment – where a product is made, costs of components, materials, manufacturing (including labour) and the transportation of the finished product

- values of society – why we wear clothes: protection, modesty, adornment; clothing, for example, has become a way of reflecting our gender, culture and religion. Some items have become unisex and suitable across society.

▌ Moral issues

Moral issues are concerned with the way in which products are manufactured and how they affect the safety, comfort and well-being of people who make them and those who come into contact with the designs/products.

Many companies now try to ensure that products are made in the right conditions, without exploiting workers, and to follow a code of practice.

Moral issues include:

- moral development – reflecting on how technology affects the environment, and the advantages and disadvantages of new technologies to local and national communities: GM foods, production automation, manufacture in developing economies

- conditions of working within a manufacturing environment – for example, job satisfaction, wages, safety of the workplace and workers.

The Ethical Trading Initiative (ETI) is an alliance of companies, non-governmental organisations (NGOs) and trade union organisations, whose aim is to promote and improve the implementation of regulated codes of practice that set out minimal working requirements. (See www.ethicaltrade.org for more information.)

Ethical companies ensure that their employees have basic labour rights; they are also careful to protect the environment in the production, packaging and distribution of their goods. Ethical companies are often termed 'sweatshop-free'. 'Sweatshop' is a term used to describe a business with poor working conditions.

The Fairtrade Foundation is an independent non-profit organisation that licenses the use of the 'FAIRTRADE Mark' on products in the UK, which meet internationally agreed Fairtrade standards set by Fairtrade Labelling Organisations International (FLO). The Foundation was established in 1992. (See www.fairtrade.org.uk for more information.)

Figure 9.10 FAIRTRADE Mark

Cultural issues

Many cultures have important traditions that form part of their identity. How do products affect the quality of lives within different cultures? The use and maintenance of traditional skills and cultural knowledge can have an impact on modern products.

Cultural issues include the following:

- considering, responding to and valuing the responses of others to design solutions
- the impact of different cultures on modern products – the use and maintenance of traditional skills and knowledge.

Culture is about the way that people behave and relate to one another. It is about the way that people live, work and spend their leisure time. It is about people's beliefs and aspirations.

Environmental issues

In a modern, fast-changing society, where products are continually being changed, it is important that you keep up to date with various issues. You will need to address the following key points within your material area:

- Understand and be able to select materials that are both suitable and sustainable.
- Be aware of the disposal and recycling of materials and components and the appropriate methods of manufacture.
- Prepare materials economically, minimising waste and using pre-manufactured standard components.
- Have knowledge of the reduction in common usage of environmentally unfriendly chemicals and materials dangerous to the environment, such as bleaches, CFCs and toxic materials. The pollution caused by manufacturing can be high, and ways to reduce this are being investigated. It is sometimes necessary to use chemicals and man-made materials which are not the most ecologically sound if the specific performance characteristic of that chemical/material is only obtained that way.

CFCs

CFCs are one of a group of synthetic substances containing chlorine and bromine, developed in the 1930s. Thought to be safe, non-flammable and non-toxic, they were widely used until the 1980s, when it was discovered that they were the main source of harm to the ozone layer.

Carbon footprint

This is a measure of the impact human activities have on the environment in terms of the amount of greenhouse gases produced through the outlet of carbon dioxide. This has an impact on global warming. A carbon footprint is linked to the ecological footprint and can be measured through transportation of materials and goods, energy use in manufacture, and the use of natural resources and renewable resources.

Figure 9.11 Carbon footprint logo

Carbon offsetting

This is a method by which people and companies can undertake measures to offset the impact they have on the environment in terms of their carbon footprint. Carbon offsetting involves contributing to the development of more ecological methods of energy generation, such as the use of renewable sources.

Reforestation

This is the term used to describe the restocking of existing forests and woodlands. The advantage of this method is that the areas restocked can provide the ecosystem with resource benefits to soak up some of the negative effects of carbon dioxide.

End-of-life disposal

This issue is linked to the need to dispose of redundant products and their packaging in a safe and environmentally friendly way. The use of labelling for specific packaging is helpful to the consumer when buying products.

Symbols used in resistant materials

Figure 9.12 Symbols used in resistant materials

Design issues

Buying a product can be expensive, so you need to ensure that you have got what you want and that it will benefit you in some way. Researching the product beforehand and analysing the information gathered can help you to come to a conclusion to ensure that your choice is successful.

ACTIVITY

1. Identify how good design and product choice improves quality of life.
2. Look at the way that designers respond to changing styles, tastes, technological advances and environmental pressures. What impact does this have?

QUESTIONS

1. How do you decide when to update your clothes or other products?

2. Why do you want to buy the latest mobile phone?

Designers are constantly changing and evolving their work. Sources of inspiration come from all areas of design and technology. In all products, new and constantly changing materials are being developed. In all the subject areas, smart materials have developed significantly over the last few years. To help you stay up to date in these areas, it would be useful to visit some of the following websites:

- www.voltaicsystems.com – new fabrics made from recycled soda bottles for solar bags
- www.ttf.co.uk – timber trade federation to protect the interests of the wood industry
- www.fsc-uk.org – management of long-term timber supplies
- www.bpf.co.uk – leading trade association for the British plastics industry
- www.c4s.info – centre for sustainability
- www.wasteonline.org.uk – recycling of many different materials
- www.recyclemetals.org – BMRA (British Metals Recycling Association)
- www.design-technology.info/alevelsubsite – click on the link 'Smart materials and their uses'
- www.designinsite.dk – click on the 'Environment' link.

Eco-design

This involves the whole system of looking at an end product, from design to finished article, and its use of materials and energy.

Eco-design is the process of designing a product from scratch with the environment in mind, and trying to minimise the damage caused to the environment by the product's life cycle. A designer must think through the following main stages if the product is to be successful and acceptable as eco-designed:

- product planning
- product development
- design process
- functionality
- safety
- ergonomics
- technical issues and requirements
- design aesthetics.

The European Ecolabel is an official label awarded to a product guaranteeing it has fulfilled specific criteria. A product awarded the Ecolabel will have been found to have a smaller environmental impact than other similar products. The Ecolabel is the official sign of environmental quality. It is awarded by independent organisations, and it is valid throughout Europe. The label's criteria aim to limit the environmental impacts of a product over its entire life cycle by looking at such issues as energy and water consumption, waste production and use of renewable resources.

Figure 9.13 European eco label

The globalisation of products

The globalisation of products is the internationalisation of products, labour and skills. Products are made in countries where specific traditions, skills and techniques which are part of people's everyday lives can offer valuable income and jobs to a previously poor area. Manufacturers can take advantage of low labour wages. Different cultures may have very different needs.

ACTIVITY

1. Working in a group, list the advantages and disadvantages you would need to be aware of when manufacturing products abroad. Remember to consider the different materials, culture and working conditions.
2. Try to list six examples of products that you know have been manufactured abroad.

▶ Summary

Many areas in this chapter are also covered in specific subject detail in other chapters in this book. Sustainable design is a world issue and a constantly changing one. You should want the world to be a great sustainable place in which to live, one that is for you, for your friends and relatives, and for future generations.

A sustainable way of designing can have an impact and a positive effect on everyone. As a designer, you need to remember and consider the social, economic and environmental implications of your decisions.

KEY TERMS

LIFE CYCLE – The stages a new product goes through, from conception to eventual decomposition.

REFORESTATION – The restocking of existing forests and woodlands.

SWEATSHOP – A business with poor working conditions.

CULTURE – The way that people behave and relate to one another; the way that people live, work and spend their leisure time; people's beliefs and aspirations.

CFCS – One of a group of synthetic substances containing chlorine and bromine, developed in the 1930s and originally thought to be safe, non-flammable and non-toxic; they were widely used until the 1980s, when it was discovered that they were the main source of harm to the ozone layer.

CHAPTER 10

UNIT A563: MAKING QUALITY PRODUCTS

By the end of this chapter you should have developed a knowledge and understanding of:

- Responding to a design brief
- Producing a design specification
- Generating and communicating design ideas
- Producing and communicating a final design proposal
- Planning the making of a product
- Making a quality product
- Solving technical problems
- Recording the stages of making a product
- Testing and evaluating the product leading to proposals for further improvement of the product.

This unit of the GCSE course requires a total of 20 hours of work and represents 30 per cent of your total marks for the GCSE qualification.

The work consists of identifying a design opportunity, generating design ideas, modelling, skilfully manufacturing a quality product and evaluating your finished product.

The coursework will develop the skills you have acquired during the first year of your GCSE course. In particular, this unit of work will use and develop skills learned in Unit A561: Introduction to Designing and Making.

The completed project can be presented either on paper or in electronic format. In both cases, the work will be marked by your teacher and moderated by OCR using the assessment criteria for this unit.

▶ Important guidelines and procedures

You should make your own judgements and decisions, and take responsibility for the direction in which your project moves. Your teacher will advise, support and assist you by suggesting approaches, alternatives and possibilities, and by directing you to appropriate resources.

Throughout the project you must remember that you will have to sign a declaration saying that the work is your own original work. Where some of the work is carried out outside the centre, it is important that your teacher is able to confirm that the work is your own. Sufficient work must be carried out under the direct supervision of your teacher for the whole of your work to be verified.

If you are working with other students on a group project, you must identify and take responsibility for uniquely definable aspects of the overall product. Ultimately, your work must constitute a complete project in its own right and provide unique evidence for assessment against each of the assessment criteria.

It is important that you acknowledge clearly the source of all information and assistance at the appropriate point in your record of designing and making. This includes extracts from newspapers, magazines, catalogues, websites, CD-ROMs, photocopied materials and practical assistance with making tasks.

▶ Assessment and submission of coursework

The project is not just about assessment and helping you to gain a qualification; it is also about you enjoying your work and 'learning by doing' this coursework project.

You should structure your work to follow the assessment criteria, and present your work in section number order.

Work submitted on paper

A contents page with a numbering system should be included to aid organisation. All your work should be on the same size paper, but it does not matter what size paper you choose. You can produce your work by hand or using ICT, but you should remember that it is the content of the work which is important and no extra marks will be gained just by word-processing your work, for example.

Work submitted electronically

Your work will need to be organised in folders so that the evidence can be accessed easily by a teacher or moderator. This structure is commonly known as a folder tree. There should be a top-level folder, detailing your centre number, candidate number, surname and forename, together with the unit code A563. The next folder down should be called 'Home Page', which will be an index of all your work. The evidence for each section of the work should then be stored in a separate folder, containing appropriately named files. These files can be from the Microsoft® Office suite, movie, audio, graphics, animation, structured markup or text formats. Microsoft PowerPoint® is an ideal platform for producing electronic portfolios.

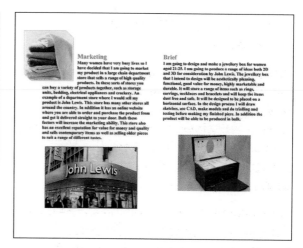

Figure 10.1 A design brief for a jewellery container

The importance of the right project choice

You will have to select a theme as a starting point for your designing and making. Your teacher will give you a list of possible starting points or may set a theme for all projects in your teaching group. When you select your area of study you must remember that you are not allowed to study the same theme that you selected for Unit A561.

Your centre may also set a common design brief as a starting point for all projects in your

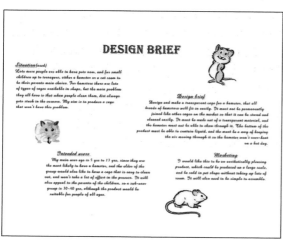

Figure 10.2 A design brief for a hamster cage

teaching group, or you may be asked to identify a design need or situation and present a design brief that is individual to you.

Typical themes

Some typical themes and starting points are listed in Table 10.1 on pahe 208. These should be used as a guide only, as the themes set by the examination board can change from year to year. Your teacher will give you a list of themes for the examination session in which you are entered.

The purpose of this project is to demonstrate your abilities in designing, making and evaluating. If you are to write your own design brief, your project will need to:

- meet a real design problem – you will need to think carefully about what is needed by the user group and not just about what you would like personally
- be challenging, to allow you to achieve the grade you are capable of, but not so difficult that you are unable to complete the work

Themes	Starting point
Entertainment	Storage for entertainment systems
Home	A storage device for equipment
Gardens	Garden products with a green focus
Family	A product to be used by a family group
My environment	A product of personal value or interest
Mechanisms	A product that includes a functioning mechanism
Adornment	Body adornment product(s) made in metal, wood or plastic
Charities	A product to help a charity in its work
The environment	An aid to help clear a litter-strewn area
Music	A product making comforting sounds

Table 10.1 Themes and starting points

- display creativity and innovation
- result in a complete high-quality product which can be evaluated
- be realistic and manageable within the time and resources available, including the expertise of your teachers.

Remember:

- you need to be realistic in your choice of project and listen to the advice of your teachers
- the size of your product is not important – small, carefully designed, well-made products will often outscore larger products
- cost of materials and pre-manufactured components can be a problem.

▌ Characteristics of a successful project

- Good planning and organisation
- Clear focus on what your target group would like
- Creativity and refinement

- High-quality work and attention to detail
- Understanding the impact your project may have on the environment
- Good use of computer-aided design in generating a design proposal and, if appropriate, good use of computer-aided manufacture in making components for your product
- Clear and careful communication and presentation

KEY POINT

- You will need to think about how you use the time you have available, making sure that you spend longer on the sections that can be awarded more marks and less time on those sections with fewer marks.

▌ Section by section

There is a maximum of 60 marks available for

this work. These 60 marks will be divided into seven sections, as shown in table 10.2.

Section	Marks
Responding to a design brief and producing a specification	4
Producing and communicating design ideas	8
Communicating the details of your design	4
Planning and making your product safely and to a high standard	24
Solving technical problems	6
Recording the making of your product	6
Evaluating your product	8

Table 10.2 Sections and marks for Unit A563

You will need to hand the following items to your teacher when you have completed the work.

Design worksheets

This will contain all of the design and evaluation work you have done. It can be submitted in paper or electronic form, but not a combination of both.

A product

This will be your final product made from resistant materials.

Digital images/photographs

These will be included as part of the design worksheets above and will include:

- a view of the front of your product
- a view of the back of your product
- views of any models or mock-ups made by you when designing and modelling
- views of the product being tested.

A cover sheet

This will be the completed OCR examination board cover sheet, which will include details of your name, school, candidate number and so on.

▶ Section 1 Responding to a design brief and producing a specification

Respond to your design brief and produce a specification for the product.

Assessment criteria	Marks
Demonstrate an appropriate and considered response to a brief and produce a detailed specification for a product as a result of analysis	4
Demonstrate an appropriate response to a brief and produce a suitable specification for a product as a result of analysis	2–3
Demonstrate a limited response to a brief and produce a simple specification for a product	0–1

Table 10.3 Assessment criteria and marks for Section 1

Responding to your design brief

A good way to start this section is to use the 5Ws method outlined in chapter 1. You will need to communicate with the user group for your product to find out exactly what they require. To do this, you can conduct a questionnaire, survey or interview and then write a conclusion about what you have found.

Other useful activities in responding to your design brief are:

- considering what social, moral, cultural and environmental issues are relevant to the product

- collecting relevant measurable information on anthropometrics, sizes, weights, capacities, quantities and costs
- collecting relevant information on safety or other consumer legislation
- collecting relevant information about pre-manufactured components, materials, constructional methods and finishes
- looking at existing products that do a similar job to your product – what features do they have? What materials, methods of construction and finishes have been used? Why have these been used?

Producing a specification

The design specification is a list of the design requirements for the product you are designing. Detailed information about specifications can be found in chapter 1 (page 10). The specification will be a conclusion to all the work you have done on the project so far. It will give you a focus for producing design ideas in section 2 of this unit, as well as a framework for testing and evaluating your product after it has been made.

Look carefully at the information you have gathered: what are the key requirements for your product? List these requirements as bullet points and make sure that your specification includes all of the following:

- performance criteria – precisely what the product has to do; properties of materials and finishes that are important; expected lifespan
- measurable details – maximum or minimum sizes, weights, capacities, quantities and costs
- aesthetics – colour, proportion and texture
- manufacturing – scale of production and economics
- user factors – ergonomics, safety, legislation, handling, storage and maintenance
- environmental aspects – the product in use and disposal.

Analysis of my Questionnaire

From studying my questionnaire I confirmed many of my initial thoughts:

- I found out from my questionnaire that the majority of the young women people who stated that they had purchased a jewellery box in the last 5 years were within the age range 21 - 25.
- I also found that the majority of people who had completed my questionnaire and stated that they probably will purchase a jewellery box in the next 4 years were also within the age range21 – 25.
- This showed that I had marketed my user group at the correct age as out of 20 young women (aged 21-25) I asked, 18 said they would purchase a jewellery box within the next 4 years.

- I found out that the majority of 21-25 year olds would expect a jewellery box to last more than 5 years and the most they would pay is £30.
- Because of these findings it is important that the jewellery box I design cost less than £30 and that will last more than 5 years.

- From asking 20 women about what they would like in a jewellery box I found out that all the young women wanted a jewellery box sized Between 100x100x100mm -200x200x200mm and the most common shapes they preferred were square and rectangle.
- This showed that many would not purchase a jewellery box that was too large and they did not like unusual shapes as these were hard to place in their bedrooms. It is important that I think about these aspects when making my design to make my jewellery box appeal to my entire user group.

- I found out that the majority of young women aged 21-25 would prefer a jewellery box made out of wood and in a modern style.
- I found that all those who chose wood as a desired material chose Walnut as a preferred wood choice.
- Therefore because of these finding it is important that my design is made from wood and ideally walnut.

- I found out that many young women would prefer a jewellery box with a pattern on the lid to make the item more aesthetically pleasing. Also many liked a natural finish like varnish or wax where they could still see the natural grain.
- Because of this it is important that my design has a pattern on the lid and does not have a finish such as paint or leather.

- I found out that the majority of young women aged 21-25 owned between 0 and 10 necklaces.

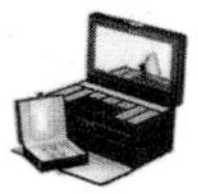

- I found out from undertaking my questionnaire that my user group owned between 0-10 bracelets and between 0 to 5 rings.
- Because of this the jewellery box I design must be able to hold at least this amount and in different compartment so the user's jeweller can be kept tidy, dust free and safe.

- I found out that many women who filled in my questionnaire would like a jewellery box to be a focal point in a room as well as being practical.
- Consequently it is vital that my jewellery box is appealing and has a nice finish as well as being useful.

- I found out that from my questionnaire that it is essential to have draws in a jewellery box to separate items.
- Many women would expect a jewellery box to have at least 2 draws.
- Many women aged 21-25 would want a tray in the top for rings and other small items of jewellery.
- Because of this draws are essential in my design so that young women can store their jewellery. It is also significant that there are at least 2 draws to separate bracelets and necklaces and a tray in the top for rings.

- I found out that many women would store their sentimental items in a jewellery box but only if it was lined.
- Therefore It is important that my draws re lined to protect the users items for getting scratched and damaged.

- I found out that the majority of people who filled out my questionnaire would like a mirror in the top of the lid even if it was only small as it would be very handy.
- In addition many women would like to be able to take the jewellery box with them went they went away for a long period of time and therefore would like a jewellery box to be fairly light in weight.
- Because of this it is important my design is made at light as possible and does have a mirror in the lid.
- I found out that there are also some extra things which women of my user group find important this they wrote in the any further comment section. One of these was that a few mentioned that they would not purchase a jewellery box that was of a shape such as a flower or heart as this they regarded as childish. In addition a few also mentioned that nice and modern handles were very important.

In conclusion the jewellery box I design must for fill as many of these ideals as possible for it to be a successful design and for it to appeal to my intended user group as much as possible. I will also use all the information I have found out to form a suitable and appropriate specification.

Figure 10.3 Conclusions from a questionnaire conducted on the user group

Before designing my product, I ask twenty musicians a few questions for guidance. I wanted to see what the public look for when buying a case. This will help me develop my designs and ideas before making the final product.

Public Response

Question	Number of people answering to:			Most Popular Answer
	A	B	C	
What do you look for in a case?	4	14	2	B. Style
What is your preferred material?	11	3	6	A. Wood
If A what finish would you prefer?	1	8	2	B. Varnish
What Shape do you look for?	10	5	5	A. Rectangular
What colour interior do you prefer?	4	12	4	B. Black
Is price a major factor when buying a case?	8	4	8	A. Yes and C. Depends on the case
Is weight a major factor when buying a case?	9	3	8	A. Yes

70% of people look for style in a case.
55% of people prefer a wooden case.
Around 72% of people prefer a varnished finish.
50% of people would prefer a rectangular case.
60% of people prefer a black interior.
40% of people think that price is a major factor when buying a case, and also 40% of people thinks that it depends on the case.
45% of people believe that weight is a major factor when buying a case.

To make my product successful with the public it must have:
- Style
- Preferably made from wood
- Use a varnish finish
- Rectangular shape
- Black interior
- Not too pricey
- Should not be too heavy

Figure 10.4 A summary of a questionnaire conducted on the user group

WHAT

My coffee table will be used for many functions. It will be used to create a welcoming and interesting focal point of the room that is aesthetically pleasing as well as obviously being useful.

It will also be used when entertaining fiends so that they have somewhere to place their glasses... so they don't have to hold them all the time. It will also be used so that if a young couple have children they have somewhere to place drinks so they aren't easily knocked over which may happen if they were placed on the floor. It will be used so that if I young couple or young family doesn't have a study where they can work and store any work. My product will enable them to work in the living room as well as giving them a drawer to store their work tidily so that they don't have to risk misplacing it or it getting accidentally chucked away with other rubbish.

Finally by using light and neutral colours my product will be used to help create a homely, cosy and stress free feel so that a young couple or young family have an area where they can relax together after a day at work.

Figure 10.5 Responding to a design brief to design and make a coffee table

Research and Specification

WHO

My product is aimed at young couples and young families. Therefore it must be a unique style that is both modern and practical. It can not be old fashioned in any way, as young adults as a whole would not tend to buy an old fashioned product as it would not appeal to them. I decided that my best aim would be to focus my product at young couples and families, as they often need to purchase a coffee table for there new homes so that they have somewhere to place glasses... especially when entertaining friends or if they have young children so that they don't get knocked over.

I felt that a suitable coffee table that is both modern and value for money would be welcomed by young couples/families, as many would find the product useful as well as it been a feature of the room. It is also important however that the table does not cost a lot of money as many young adults and families may not have a lot of money as they may have just left university and might be in debt or they may have just purchased a house together. Therefore if it is too expensive they will not be able to afford it. My product will sell better to young families that an older generation as it will be more appealing to them and also more useful.

Finally my product my product must appeal and be suitable for both sexes as it is to be placed in a living room that is share by both sexes.

WHERE

The product I am designing will be purchased to be used in young couples/families living rooms. As often a young couple or young family's first home together is quite small and therefore the rooms are quite small, the coffee table I will design will have to be made so that it is suitable for that type of space. For that reason my coffee table will be small enough so that it doesn't take up too much valuable floor space. As if I was to make a coffee table that was too large it would not sell as well, because it would take up too much valuable floor space and therefore would not be suitable for this type of room. I also decided against designing a coffee table that is too heavy as for several reasons; for example if a young family had children they might want to be able to move it around so that they could create space for the children to play, and this would not be easily possible if it was so heavy.

If my product is designed so it is suitable to be placed in a small living room it will be more marketable and profitable, as more young families and young couples will purchase it as they can decide where in the room they want it and where it will look the best with out it taking up too much of floor space.

WHY

Many young couples and young families use their lounges for entertaining friends, discussing aspects of their work as well as the usual day to day activities such as watching the television.

Young couples therefore will purchase this product because it enables them to use it for several functions. A coffee table can change the way a room looks it can make a room look more welcoming and a pleasant space to relax. Another reason why this coffee table might be used is to give the room a focal point. Many young couples' living rooms look very similar with a sofa and a television so this is a way for them to create a focal point in their room that is not too expensive, is aesthetically pleasing and suitable as well as being useful. Many young couples/families can also afford to buy a house with a study, so many will want to do work in their living room a coffee table will also give them a place to store their work in one place, tidily. A coffee table will make the room feel more homely which is nice as if it is their first home together it might be the first time they have lived away from parents.

Finally many young families might be worried about young children knocking over drinks so this would enable adult to have a stable place to put their drinks with less risk of them being spilt.

WHEN

My table will be used all the time as a focal point in the room so it must be aesthetically pleasing as well as obviously being practical. It will also be used a lot of the time for functional purposes. They will use it when entertaining friends, so that it not only helps to create a welcoming feel to the room but also sop that their guests have some where to place their cups/glasses. It will also be used if the young couple has children so that their drinks won't get knocked over so easily. It may be used if a couple doesn't have a study in their home and has to do some work from home as it would give them a flat surface to work on as well as giving them an area where they can store their work away safely an tidily.

Finally they may use the coffee table to put food on if the wished to have a meal in front of the television with their partner.

SPECIFICATION

THE CASE MUST:

- **PROTECTION**- The guitar must be safe. The guitar case must be made from strong attractive material of a substantial quality so that the owner can feel sure that their guitar is safe from harm and any contact with rough surfaces.
- **TRANSPORT**-The case must be easily transportable and comfortable to hold, the shape must be unique but not a nuisance to carry around.
- **SAFETY**- This guitar case must meet all BSI safety standards, the product must be safe for its user and the area in which it will be used or stored, and this will give the public confidence in the product and assure them that it is of a very high quality.

- **DESIGN**-The products design must be stylish and eye catching, I want my product to be unique to its rivals but the design would have to suit and appeal to a range of age groups.
- **EXTRAS**-This product must have smart components and extras to complement the case.
- **COST**-The case should at least be under thirty seven pounds (£37).I would believe that if the product was too over priced it wouldn't sell to a numeral amount of customers, but if my product was too under priced customers may think it to be cheap and of a low quality.
- **DURABILITY**-This case must have a guaranty of over two years.
- **USE**-The product is used to transport a guitar from one destination to another.
- **FINISH**- I will use a neat finish for a clean and smart appearance.
- **BATCH**-It must be suitable for batch production using jigs, stencils etc. for repetitive accuracy.
- **Weight**- The product must not be heavier than 10kg

Figure 10.6 A specification for a guitar case

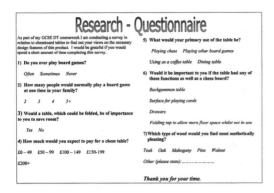

Figure 10.7 A questionnaire conducted on the user group to find information about the design of a chess table

Assessment criteria	Marks
• Produce creative and original ideas by generating, developing and communicating design using a range of appropriate strategies	6–8
• Produce creative ideas and communicate these by using appropriate strategies	3–5
• Produce one or two simple design ideas using a limited range of strategies	0–2

Table 10.4 Assessment criteria and marks for Section 2

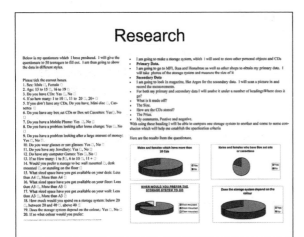

Figure 10.8 The questions and some results of a questionnaire about a CD storage system

Section 2 Producing and communicating design ideas

Create design ideas and communicate them using a range of appropriate techniques.

When you start designing, you need to think of as many ideas as you can and record them with simple drawings that you can look at again later. The more ideas you put down, the better, as the more ideas you have, the more likely it is that one of them is a really good one.

Put ideas down quickly, think as widely as you can and do not worry if your ideas seem a bit crazy at first.

You should annotate your ideas to:

- communicate features of an idea which you think are particularly promising
- highlight features of the idea that could be a problem and require further thought
- show overall sizes
- show ideas for materials that could be used
- show ideas for methods of construction that could be used
- show ideas for finishes that could be used.

Remember that there are marks for communicating your designs using a range of different methods. Some of the techniques you may wish to use include:

- simple 2D and 3D pencil sketches
- 3D drawings using coloured pencils or marker pens for shading
- computer-generated 2D modelling

- 3D models using card or other modelling materials to develop your ideas further.

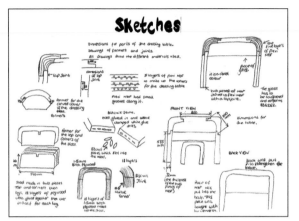

Figure 10.9 Some design ideas for a table and stool

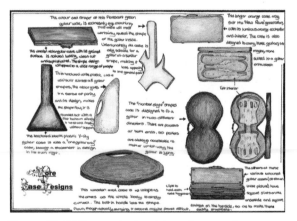

Figure 10.10 Some design ideas for a guitar case

▶ Section 3 Communicating the details of your design

Produce detailed and annotated drawings to communicate all details of your chosen design proposal.

You will need to show all the information that is required to enable your product to be made. A combination of drawings and notes will be necessary. The usual drawing method

Assessment criteria	Marks
Use detailed drawings and annotation clearly to communicate all details of the design chosen for prototype production	4
Use drawing and annotation to communicate most details of the design chosen for prototype production	2–3
Use drawing and annotation to communicate limited and incomplete details of the design chosen for prototype production	0–1

Table 10.5 Assessment criteria and marks for Section 3

for a final design is orthographic projection, but you can use any method of drawing as long as your drawings and notes show:

- the shape of each component to be made
- the size of each component to be made
- the materials to be used for each component
- details of the finish to be used on each component

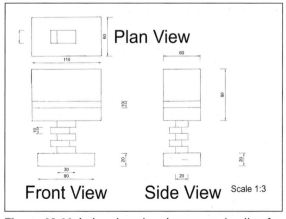

Figure 10.11 A drawing showing some details of a lamp design

- details of any pre-manufactured components
- details of the methods and processes used to assemble the product.

Section 4 Planning and making your product safely and to a high standard

You need to plan very carefully how you are going to make your product. This will involve writing a step-by-step plan for making each component, to include:

- the tools and equipment to be used

- details of any safety precautions that need to be taken at each stage
- an estimate of how long each stage will take – this can be set out in a table, as shown in chapter 1 (page 22).

You will also need to plan the quality assurance methods you will require and the stages at which you will need quality control.

You will see from the assessment criteria in Table 10.6 that to gain high marks you will need to:

- select materials, tools and equipment carefully

Assessment criteria	Marks

• Plan and organise activities:
  – select and use appropriate materials
  – select and use hand and machine tools as appropriate to the material area
• Work skilfully and safely to shape, form, assemble and finish materials or components as appropriate
• Assess and apply knowledge in the workshop facilities as appropriate to working with resistant materials
• The product will be completed to a high standard and will fully meet the requirements of the final product specification
	18–24

• Plan and organise activities:
  – select and use appropriate materials
  – select and use hand and machine tools as appropriate to the material area
• Work effectively and safely to shape, form, assemble and finish materials or components as appropriate
• Select and use workshop facilities as appropriate to working with resistant materials
• The product will be completed to a good standard and will meet most of the requirements of the final product specification
	10–17

• Plan and organise activities:
  – select and use appropriate materials
  – select and use hand and machine tools as appropriate to the material area
• Work safely to shape, form, assemble and finish materials or components as appropriate
• Use workshop facilities as appropriate to working with resistant materials
• The product will exhibit a low standard of outcome and may not be successfully completed
	0–9

Table 10.6 Assessment criteria and marks for Section 4

- work skilfully to make your product, using the facilities in your centre's workshops.

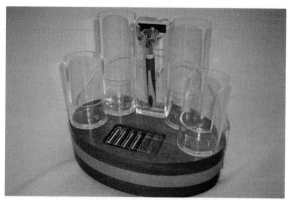

Figure 10.12 A well-made shaving stand

WHAT YOU NEED TO DO

- Select materials, tools and equipment to make your product.
- Produce a step-by-step plan to make your product.
- Work skilfully and safely to make a product using resistant materials, to meet the requirements of the product specification.

Section 5 Solving technical problems

Demonstrate how you have solved technical problems as they arise.

Assessment criteria	Marks
Demonstrate a practical and thorough understanding in the solving of technical problems effectively and efficiently as they arise	5–6
Demonstrate a practical understanding and ability in the solving of some technical problems as they arise	3–4
Demonstrate a simple understanding of how to solve technical problems as they arise	0–2

Table 10.7 Assessment criteria and marks for Section 5

Technical problems are likely to arise in two different ways:

- technical problems that have been foreseen before the product is made
- technical problems that have only come to light during the manufacture of the product.

Stage by Stage

Stage Number	Stage	Tools and Equipment used	Safety	Time taken to complete stage
1	Plane wood to correct width and thickness	Smoothing plane.	Wear goggles and overalls, make sure all hair is tied back and secure	2 hours
2	Cut wood to length	Tenon saw, sanding disk.	Take of loose clothing such as ties, wear eye protection. Hair must be tied back.	1 hour
3	Mark out joins	Marking knif, marking gage, tri-square, pencil, steel rules.	Care with marking knife	1 hour
4	Cut joints	Tenon saw, chisel.	Care with sharp edge on chisel and saw. Wear goggles and overall at all times.	1 hour
5	Cut groves for top and base etc.	Plough plane.	Care with plan, wear goggles and eye protection. Keep fingers well away.	1 hour
6	Sand inside surfaces	Glass paper, cork block.	Use clamps to clamp down work securely before sanding.	2 hours
7	Glue together	G-clamps, PVA glue.	Make sure surfaces are clean before applying glue. Wash hands after using glue.	½ hour
8	Cut lid from base	Tenon saw.	Wear goggles and overalls at all time, care with sharp blade.	1 hour
9	Make handles	Lathe, glass paper.	Important to have no loose clothes or hair, wear goggles and overall.	1 hour
10	Fix hinges, clasp and handles	Electrical drill to drill holes, chisel, screw driver.	Wear goggles when using electric drill, care with sharp edge on chisel.	½ hour
11	Sand outside surfaces	Glass paper, cork block.	Using clamps to clamp down work securely before sanding.	1 hour
12	Wax all surfaces including inside lid	Cloth, beeswax.	Wash hands thoroughly after use.	1 hour
13	Cut velvet to fit inside the tray and drawers	Scissor, pen, steel rules.	Care with sharp scissors when cutting the material.	1 hour
14	Mark out lining timber	Merking knife, tri square, metre square.	Care with marking knife.	1 hour
15	Cut lining timber to correct size	Tenon saw, sanding disk.	Take of loose clothing such as ties, wear eye protection. Hair must be tied back.	1 ½ hour
16	Fix lining timber	G-clamps, PVA glue.	Make sure surfaces are clean before applying glue. Wash hands after using glue.	1 hour
17	Fix in mirror	Double sided tape, scissors.	Wear overalls, care when using scissors.	½ hour
18	Cut top design using CAD/CAM machine	2D design, TF 400.	Watch for sharp edges after been cut.	½ hour
19	Wax final pettern design before fixing it on	Cloth, beeswax.	Wash hands after use, wear overalls.	½ hour
20	Fix on design to top of lid	G-clamps, PVA glue.	Make sure surfaces are clean before applying glue. Wash hand after using glue.	½ hour
			Total time taken	10 ½ hour

Figure 10.13 A production plan for a jewellery container

You should therefore record:

- how you solved any technical problems as the product was developed from an initial idea to a final design proposal for production

- any changes that have been made to your final design proposal as the product was being made.

You should not be concerned if you need to make changes to your final design, as things do not always go entirely to plan, even for the most experienced designers. It is far more important to solve problems if they arise rather than to ignore them.

▶ Section 6 Recording the making of your product

Record the key stages in making your product, using notes and photographic evidence.

Assessment criteria	Marks
Record key stages involved in the making of the product; provide comprehensive notes and photographic evidence	5–6
Record key stages involved in the making of the product; provide notes and photographic evidence	3–4
Simply record the making of the product, using notes and/or photographic evidence	0–2

Table 10.8 Assessment criteria and marks for Section 6

You need to keep a record or log of all the stages of making your product. This will include some or all of the following:

- marking out materials
- cutting out each component
- marking out holes and/or joints
- cutting holes and/or joints
- details of quality assurance or quality control checks used
- details of finishing techniques and applied finishes used
- details of each stage of the product's assembly.

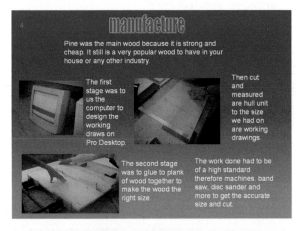

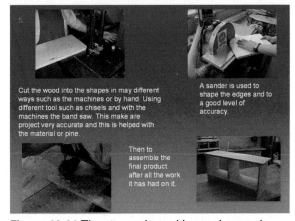

Figure 10.14 The stages in making a shoe rack

You will need to do this using notes and sketches, and take photographs of the operations listed above as they are carried out. If you are going to present your work in electronic format, you can also use short sections of video to show operations such as a laser cutter producing a component.

Section 7 Evaluating your work

- Test your product in use and present conclusions.

- Evaluate your product against the specification.

- Produce proposals for modifications to improve your product.

Now that the making of your project has been completed, you need to test it to see how well it fulfils the requirements of your design specification. The product needs to be tested by the intended user in the intended situation and location. You should devise a

KEY POINT

- Unlike the evaluation section of unit A561, this section requires you to evaluate the **product** itself and make proposals about how it could be further improved. You are not commenting on the project as a whole or the process of designing and making.

series of tests to determine how well the product performs, in use, when it is transported and when it is stored. Remember that the most important aspect to test is if the product does the job it is supposed to do. Some things will be difficult to test, such as how long the product will last and the

Assessment criteria	Marks
• Critically evaluate the finished product against the specification • Undertake detailed testing; present meaningful conclusions leading to proposals for modification to improve the prototype product • Specialist terms will be used appropriately and correctly • The information will be presented in a structured format • The candidate can demonstrate the accurate use of spelling, punctuation and grammar	6–8
• Give an evaluation of the finished product with reference to the specification • Show superficial testing and reflect on how to improve the product • There will be some use of specialist terms, although these may not always be used appropriately • The information will be presented for the most part in a structured format • There may be occasional errors in spelling, punctuation and grammar	3–5
• Give a limited evaluation of the finished product, with some reference to the specification • There is no evidence of testing the product in use • There will be little or no use of specialist terms • Answers may be ambiguous or disorganised • Errors of spelling, punctuation and grammar may be intrusive	0–2

Table 10.9 Assessment criteria and marks for Section 7

aesthetic qualities of the product. A good way of assessing these qualities is to ask the opinions of people who have experience with the sort of product you have produced.

You will need to look at each point on your specification and make a judgement about how well your product performs based on the tests you have undertaken.

Finally, you should consider what further improvements could be made to your product in the light of the tests you have carried out. These improvements may include:

- modifications to the size or form of the components used in your product
- any changes to pre-manufactured components you would make
- changes to constructional methods used
- changes to any of the materials used
- changes to the finishes used
- additional quality assurance measures you may need to improve the product
- additional quality control tests you may need to improve the product.

Figure 10.15 Testing a jewellery box

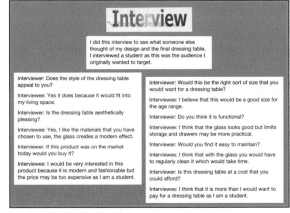

Figure 10.16 A record of an interview conducted in the process of evaluating a dressing table

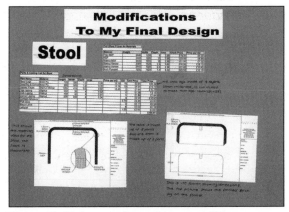

Figure 10.17 Suggestions about possible modifications to a stool in the light of evaluation

CHAPTER 11

UNIT A564: TECHNICAL ASPECTS OF DESIGNING AND MAKING

By the end of this chapter you should have developed a knowledge and understanding of:

- the structure of the exam papers
- effective examination technique
- the 'command' words used in the exam papers.

The unit A564 examination lasts for 1 hour and 15 minutes and it is worth 20 per cent of your GCSE marks. It is externally marked and is intended to be taken at the end of your course.

The paper consists of five questions that focus on the technical aspects of designing and making.

Section A consists of three questions based on the technical aspects of working with materials, tools and equipment.

Section B consists of two questions on the design of products reflecting the wider aspects of sustainability and human use. At least one of these questions will require a design response.

The questions are each worth 12 marks, giving a total of 60 marks.

The first questions are comparatively easy, but questions become progressively more difficult.

One of the questions will be marked with an asterisk (*). In this question, the 'quality of your written communication' will also be assessed.

▶ How can I achieve my best in the Unit 4 examination?

Think of Design and Technology: Resistant Materials as the practical experiences of designing and making. You will have spent many hours working with materials, tools, equipment, machines and computers, and this practical experience is the most effective way of learning about the subject. However, you need to support these activities with a range of resources, including notes, handouts, research, tests and homework. You will have been given a folder/book for the whole course to keep this work safe. Do try to keep your work in an organised way so that you can use it for revision. Use section dividers and use the chapters from this book as a guideline.

Examination success depends on a variety of factors, including:

- revision – this is very important
- practice – take every opportunity to practise examination papers, as this will develop your examination technique
- understanding of the 'command' words that are used in examination papers.

The exam questions require you to answer in a variety of ways: one-word answers, short sentences, completing tables, using sketches and notes, and giving detailed explanations.

Whichever type of answer is required, you need to look carefully at the number of marks available, as this reflects the amount of time or detail expected of you for a good answer. The number of marks will be shown in brackets [ ] at the end of each question or part of a question. You should not spend too much time on questions that carry one or two marks, or provide superficial answers to questions that carry four or five marks.

You need to:

- be really familiar with the style, layout and requirements of the papers; you should have worked on past papers
- make your thinking totally clear, and ensure that nothing is left open to interpretation by the examiner
- read through each question carefully before you start to answer; you must be clear about what the question is asking you to do and how you are to answer
- apply specific design and technology knowledge rather than general knowledge, and try to use technical terminology accurately.

▶ Command words

'State ...', 'Name ...', 'Give ...'

This requires the specific name of, for example, a tool, process, construction or material. Normally, a one- or two-word answer will be sufficient.

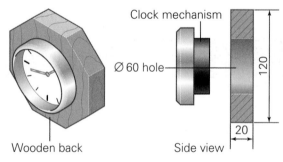

Figure 11.1

(1) Figure 11.1 shows a clock that will be hung on a wall. The clock has a mechanism that fits into a hole in the wooden back.

Example questions:

(a) State **one** safety precaution you would take when using a sanding machine. [1]

(b) Name a suitable hardwood for the wooden back. [1]

(c) Give a reason for your choice of hardwood. [1]

'Describe ...'

This requires you to give an idea of, for example, how something works, what is involved in a process or specific features of a design. It usually involves writing one or two sentences.

Example question:
(d) Describe how the Ø60 mm hole could be cut in the wooden back. [2]

'Complete ...'

This requires you to complete, for example, a design, drawing or table.

Example question:
(e) Complete Table 11.1 by describing what each of the tools or items of equipment are used for when making the wooden back. [4]

'Use sketches and notes to ...'

This is used to invite you to produce a design to solve a specific problem. It is essential that sketches are used as the main part of the answer and that they are large and clear. The written notes must support and expand on the sketches and they must be technically accurate.

These questions sometimes have a high mark allocation of five or six marks.

These questions often include a list of bulleted specification points to help you focus on the important parts of the design. Marks will be awarded when each specification point has been met in the design solution.

Example question:
(f) The clock will be hung on a wall. Use sketches and notes to show how this could be done. Include details of any fittings you would use. [3]

'Explain ...'

This requires a detailed account of something, including reasons, justifications, and possibly comparisons and examples. This type of question always carries at least two

Tool or item of equipment	What is each of the tools or items of equipment used for?
Template	
Tenon saw	
Sanding machine	
Varnish	

Table 11.1

marks. In the example below, you would need to compare both methods of manufacture in order to justify your choice.

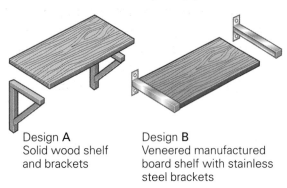

Design **A**
Solid wood shelf
and brackets

Design **B**
Veneered manufactured
board shelf with stainless
steel brackets

Figure 11.2

(2) Figure 11.2 shows **two** different shelf and bracket designs. Both designs are manufactured and sold as self-assembly products.

Example question:

(a) Explain which of the two designs would be more expensive to manufacture in quantity. [2]

'Discuss ...'

When you are asked to discuss something, you must give well-reasoned points and explanations, adding examples to show the examiner what you are thinking. One-word answers are not acceptable. You need to practise these types of questions, which are the most difficult.

There are usually six marks for this part of the question and these are split as follows:

- three marks for three relevant points
- two marks for the quality of your explanation
- one mark for a specific example to support your answer.

Example question:

(b) Discuss the impact that self-assembly has had on the design of many household products. [6]

Answering the question

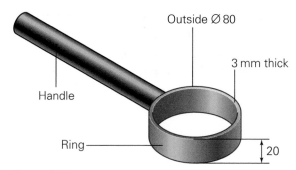

Outside Ø 80

3 mm thick

Handle

Ring

20

Figure 11.3

Example question:

(3) Figure 11.3 shows an incomplete design for a hand-held device used to unscrew different size lids from jars and bottles.

(a) Use sketches and notes to complete the device so that it:

- adjusts to fit different sized lids
- grips the lids effectively
- includes ergonomic considerations.

Include details of materials and fittings used. [8]

It is vital when you answer a design-type question with a large allocation of marks that you read the question carefully and answer each requirement. The examiner will reward each of the bullet points, so make sure that each of these points is clear in your answer. In addition, questions often end with 'Include details of materials and fittings used', so ensure that you address this thoroughly. Name specific materials, say why they are appropriate, and provide accurate information about construction, assembly or finish.

From the examples given you should be able to see how the questions become increasingly difficult throughout the paper.

Finally, examiners will not give any marks to answers such as 'strong', 'cheap', 'quick' or 'easy'. These terms on their own are meaningless. To gain a mark they need to be justified. For example, a joint could be 'strong' enough to take the weight of the tabletop; a softwood could be relatively 'cheap' when compared with hardwoods; injection-moulding is a 'quick' process once the moulds have been manufactured; a finish could be 'easy' to apply because it can be painted on straight from the tin, without stirring.

INDEX